CU00656523

Mike Dales went out on "nature walks" wi
age of three. The seed was sown, and walkii
passions ever since. His nature walks in adult life have taken him to the Himalaya, Andes, Alps and Scottish Highlands, but he traces his love of the outdoors all the way back to the paths and woodlands of East Yorkshire in the early 1960s.

His interests in hillwalking, sea kayaking, skiing, cycling and running led him to Scotland and the wide-open spaces of the Highlands and Islands. Now living in rural Perthshire, he has climbed all of Scotland's mountains known as Munros and Corbetts, and cycled from Land's End to John O'Groats and the Irish end-to-end equivalent from Mizen to Malin. A keen hill runner, his favourite forms of running are the alpine activities of uphill marathons and Vertical Kilometre races, although he is more regularly seen at parkruns and can occasionally be spotted running indoor 800 metres races in the winter season.

In 2013, Mike and his partner Fiona turned their activities into an exercise streak that has, to date, gone unbroken for over eight years. *Find Time for Exercise* begins with the story of that exercise streak, then goes into the exercise challenges that a range of Mike's friends and contacts have taken on, and ends with a call to action for the reader to think about taking on an exercise challenge as a way to improve their own health and well-being.

What began as a childhood bonding session with his grandfather has developed into a passion for taking exercise in the great outdoors and promoting the benefits of regular physical activity to wide ranging audiences.

Photograph by John-James Greig

Follow on Social Media

- Twitter: @FindTime4Xrcise
- Facebook: /FindTimeForExercise
- Instagram: /findtimeforexercise
- YouTube: FindTimeForExercise

For further information or to arrange a speaking event, please visit:

www.findtimeforexercise.com

ENDORSEMENTS

Professor Chris Oliver *is a retired trauma orthopaedic surgeon from the Royal Infirmary of Edinburgh and previous Professor of Physical Activity from Edinburgh University & King James Professor Royal College of Surgeons of Edinburgh.*
Twitter @CyclingSurgeon

Find Time for Exercise shows everybody how we can get all the health benefits from physical activity. In our modern age we are only just beginning to realise why reducing sedentary behaviour is so important. It is well known that people who partake in regular physical activity will have improved metabolic health and a reduced risk of premature mortality. Your longevity to an extent, apart from your genes and environment is determined by how physically active you can be throughout your life. There's little point driving to the gym in a car to run on a treadmill, you must be able to think beyond that idea. Mike Dales' book helps you think far beyond the car ride.

Significantly, *Find Time for Exercise* describes how physical activity reduces the risk factors for several diseases, including cardiovascular disease, respiratory disease, some cancers, and type 2 diabetes. I don't think people really appreciate that physical activity also has such profound positive effects on mental health and general well-being. The mental health and neurological benefits include reduced risk of dementia, improved sleep quality, and a greater sense of well-being. Also, in environmental terms, health benefits accrue for the general population from a reduction in pollution due to car use and a decrease in road congestion. The overall evidence is that the health benefits of physical activity described in *Find Time for Exercise* outweigh any potential health risks and harms - for example from injury or pollution whilst cycling.

Find Time for Exercise is an essential and worthwhile read, especially if you want to live longer!

https://cyclingsurgeon.bike/
https://twitter.com/CyclingSurgeon

John 'Yogi' Hughes *played professional football for several clubs including Celtic and Hibernian in a lengthy playing career. He then went on to manage a number of clubs including Hibernian and Inverness Caledonian Thistle, where he led the club to success in the 2015 Scottish Cup Final.*

As a professional footballer of over 20 years, I had the privilege to play for some fantastic football clubs. When I look back on this period of my life and the physical activity that was done on a daily basis - I was an elite athlete with a required body fat percentage of 10%. Now those football days are long gone, my levels of activity have changed - and I'm certainly not the elite athlete I once was. However, physical activity is still high on my everyday agenda, it's part of my DNA. From the tough days, it's programmed in that it needs to get done, a good habit which I get a glow of achievement from completing.

Mike Dales' *Find Time for Exercise* will give you a great insight into the importance of physical activity. The book guides you and inspires you to achieve your goals.

The way Mike tells his story about his own exercise, particularly his 5K every day of the year - the descriptions made me smile. A word of warning though, be careful when reading about Mike's exploits in *Quirky and Amusing* that it doesn't land you in trouble!!

There are lots of inspirational stories and challenges that inspire, from all ages. Stories that pull on the heart strings - my personal favourite from Agnes, one that really hit home.

Find Time for Exercise is a go-to read if you're looking for inspiration and guidance in your quest for a fitter and healthier life.

Find Time for Exercise

How to challenge yourself and enjoy
the benefits of regular exercise

MIKE DALES

Copyright © 2021 Mike Dales

The moral right of the author has been asserted.

Apart from any fair dealing for the purposes of research or private study,
or criticism or review, as permitted under the Copyright, Designs and Patents
Act 1988, this publication may only be reproduced, stored or transmitted, in
any form or by any means, with the prior permission in writing of the
publishers, or in the case of reprographic reproduction in accordance with
the terms of licences issued by the Copyright Licensing Agency. Enquiries
concerning reproduction outside those terms should be sent to the publishers.

Matador
9 Priory Business Park,
Wistow Road, Kibworth Beauchamp,
Leicestershire. LE8 0RX
Tel: 0116 279 2299
Email: books@troubador.co.uk
Web: www.troubador.co.uk/matador
Twitter: @matadorbooks

ISBN 978 180046 436 0

British Library Cataloguing in Publication Data.
A catalogue record for this book is available from the British Library.

Printed and bound by CPI Group (UK) Ltd, Croydon, CR0 4YY
Typeset in 11pt Adobe Garamond Pro by Troubador Publishing Ltd, Leicester, UK

Matador is an imprint of Troubador Publishing Ltd

"Those who do not find time for exercise will have to find time for illness."

Edward Smith-Stanley

Physical inactivity is the modern-day scourge and the chair a weapon of mass destruction – to thrive and survive we have to challenge ourselves to become more physically active – we all need to Find Time for Exercise.

This book is for all the people willing to challenge themselves, even in the smallest of ways, to become more physically active and respond positively to the call to Find Time for Exercise.

Find Time for Exercise

This book has been written with the belief that most people could benefit from an increase in their level of physical activity. However, if you have any concerns about the possible effects of exercise on your health, please consult your doctor before setting out on a new exercise regime. The author is not liable in any manner whatsoever for any adverse effect or loss occasioned to any person arising directly or indirectly from, or in connection with, the information provided in this book.

Find out more about the author and finding time for exercise at: findtimeforexercise.com

Follow on social media:

Twitter: @FindTime4Xrcise
Facebook: /FindTimeForExercise
Instagram: /findtimeforexercise
YouTube: FindTimeForExercise

Contents

Contents

Foreword

Sean Conway

Sean Conway is a well-known endurance adventurer who became the first person to separately cycle, swim and run from Land's End to John O'Groats. The swimming journey made headline news when Sean became the first person to swim the length of Great Britain, famously growing a thick ginger beard to prevent jellyfish stings.

In 2016, he completed the world's longest triathlon, a 4,200-mile journey around the coast of Britain. Then in 2018, Sean broke the record for the fastest cycle journey across Europe, making the 3,980-mile trip from Portugal to Russia in 24 days, 18 hours and 39 minutes.

Sean's achievements are so impressive, you might assume he's always been a fit and healthy sportsman with boundless energy, but that is far from the case.

Back when I was a school portrait photographer, I did absolutely no exercise at all. In fact, for most of my entire 20s I didn't own a pair of running shoes, I never went to the gym, and never played any team sports on the weekends. The closest I think I ever came to something that involved exercise was running to catch the Number 13 bus down to the photo lab where I worked part-time to pay the bills.

Needless to say, after ten years of this level of inactivity I came to the realisation that I was unfit, unmotivated and lacked any drive in life. I was miserable. Something needed to change, and I decided to work on three principles that I still use to this day.

When I'm feeling a bit low, dull, fogged-up in my head, I know that I've not been keeping to my three golden rules. These aren't instant fixes; they are long-term rules. They are: eat better, get fitter and spend more time outside in natural light. It really is that simple.

The one way to make sure you get all three of those is to take more exercise. When you exercise you will naturally get fitter and spend more time outdoors, then all that's left is to enjoy your improved appetite and eat more healthily.

Since I made this decision in my life, I've somehow gone on to become a world record breaking endurance adventure athlete, and even to this day I still can't believe I was capable of it all. The positivity and strength I have to push myself all stemmed from that early decision to find time for exercise. It seems such a simple idea, and that's because – it is.

I wish everyone knew the benefits; so when I heard about Mike's book, *Find Time for Exercise*, I immediately wanted to add my stamp of approval, because it's exactly what I believe in.

Preface

This book is aimed at everyone, absolutely everyone, including you.

It is a passionate promotion of the benefits of regular exercise and in particular the benefits of adopting an exercise challenge, however modest it might be, to help you stay motivated.

I am not an Olympic champion, international footballer or renowned mountaineer, just someone who loves being active and wants to share his passion with you.

Whether you are male or female, young or old, fit, unfit or somewhere in-between, this book is for you. It doesn't push any specific type of exercise challenge and it certainly doesn't matter what level of fitness you currently have. That's because it is not a book about competitive sport, but about exercise and the physical and mental health benefits that can be gained from taking regular exercise.

I've already mentioned the word *exercise* several times, but please think of exercise in its widest possible sense, or read it as *activity* or *movement* if those words are more appropriate for you. I don't want anyone to be put off by a mere word. If this book encourages you to move more, then it has done its job.

This is a self-help book aimed at helping anyone to become more active than they currently are, no matter where they are on the spectrum between totally inactive and superfit. All the stories in this book are of people who have moved along that spectrum and increased their activity levels, some by a small amount and others by more than they imagined they were capable of.

Please don't be discouraged by those who are going beyond what you can ever imagine yourself doing. Instead, try to pick out the pieces of advice they're giving and think about how you could apply those ideas into your own situation.

So, I invite you to come on this journey with me, and I hope you will be inspired to find time for exercise and set your own exercise challenge, however small or great. You might just be amazed at what you can achieve.

Health warning

This book promotes the benefits of regular exercise, but the author acknowledges that exercise, or a sudden increase in an individual's level of exercise, can lead to health problems including injury, illness and even death.

If you are in any doubt about your body's ability to cope with an increase in your current level of physical activity, then sensible advice is to seek guidance from your doctor.

A likely cause of doubt may arise because of an underlying health condition that you are already aware of, in which case the recommendation to seek a professional opinion from a doctor is one that the author would endorse.

Also, if you start to increase your exercise levels and feel any discomfort that concerns you, then it would be a sensible precaution to seek your doctor's advice at that point.

Here is a list of four warning signs that you should be particularly on the lookout for:

- Chest pain
- Shortness of breath
- Dizziness
- Joint pain

In each case, try to be aware of what is normal for you and try to be alert to changes that you wouldn't expect or which you find difficult to explain. For example, if you have exerted yourself a lot in recent days you may get short of breath more easily than usual, but if you find yourself out of breath after some very easy exercise, then you may want to seek a doctor's opinion as to why that might be, especially if you wouldn't normally get out of breath as quickly as that.

If you are in any doubt, seek medical advice.

Please take this health warning seriously, but, and this is a big

BUT

be aware that the greatest risk is not to risk. The greatest risk to the vast majority of people right now stems from the debilitating effects of physical inactivity, such as weight gain and a range of physical and mental health problems.

To go for a walk is to risk spraining an ankle by stepping in a rabbit hole, to go out on a bike is to risk falling off, and to go for a run is to risk tripping over an out-of-control dog, but to stay indoors and watch television is to risk putting on weight, succumbing to loneliness and depression, losing mobility in your joints and slowly, imperceptibly, falling into human disrepair and decay.

I've looked at that risk assessment myself and chosen to get outdoors for some exercise at every opportunity. I hope you will make the same assessment and arrive at the same conclusion.

- Just to throw in an additional consideration, it is worth

thinking about this simple fact from the Royal Society for the Prevention of Accidents (RoSPA)[1]: "The home is the most common location for an accident to happen".

Dr Mike Evans' video

After reading this health warning section, I would really encourage you to go onto YouTube and watch the video by Dr Mike Evans[2] titled: *24 hour fitness - 23 and ½ hours*. Mike Evans is a doctor in Canada and his amusing five-minute video sums up the power of exercise in a beautiful way. It really is the ideal accompaniment to this book and I highly recommend you find time to watch it today.

Introduction

There's a five-kilometre road circuit that I've cycled more times than I'm able to remember. The roads are quiet, rural, scenic and there's one short climb, just enough to get the legs and heart pumping. It's my regular cycle route for when I just want to get out for some quick exercise. I enjoy it every time and I'm able to vary it. For instance, I usually go round anti-clockwise, but sometimes I just decide to go the other way to take in a steeper hill. Then there are various spurs off the circuit, so I'm able to turn it into a longer ride when I have a bit more time or get the sudden urge to stay out and play a while longer.

Having ridden it so many times, my various journeys now just merge into one big memory bank of riding it in all weathers and at all times of year. One particular ride round the circuit, which I have no recollection of now, bar an entry in my diary and on my spreadsheet, was on Monday, 25 March 2013. Although I didn't know it then, that was the start of a very long and adventurous journey. That was day one of my five kilometres a day challenge.

Over eight years later, the challenge is still going. I have an unbroken run of over 3,000 consecutive days of always making an active journey of at least five kilometres every single day. It's a great challenge and I'm loving the exercise and the many benefits I take from it. Furthermore, and this is the main reason for writing this book, my exercise challenge has really sparked my interest in the way other people are challenging themselves to be more active, and that in turn has led me to develop a strong desire to encourage others to find their equivalent challenge.

My appeal to you is to consider what might be an appropriate challenge for you to take on. It doesn't matter how modest it might be. If it involves you being more active than you are at present, then you are likely to benefit from that extra exercise. So, please work your way through this book, read about the background to the way inactivity is such a danger to the human body (Part 1), take inspiration from my challenge (Part 2) and those of the other people that I interviewed for this book (Part 3), and look at the broad spectrum of other challenges (Part 4) that are available for you to adopt or adapt. The culmination of this book (Part 5) is when I help you to find a way of challenging yourself and hopefully moving you along that spectrum towards being a more active and healthier version of yourself. You'll see you are not alone, and that the rewards are achievable, no matter what your starting point.

Why you should read this book

This book is about the benefits of taking regular exercise and is aimed at inspiring you to set yourself an exercise challenge. Don't panic and please don't run away at the prospect of going for a run. I'm not advocating compulsory marathon running or outdoor swimming. However, the general trend over the last fifty or so years has been for more and more people in the developed world to adopt an increasingly sedentary lifestyle. The average amount of exercise we take is going down and all the available evidence suggests the consequence of this inactivity is taking its toll on our physical and mental health, as well as costing our health services (National Health Service (NHS) in the UK) millions in treating us for the range of ailments caused by too much sitting and too little movement. This issue is also acting to increase the cost of private health care in many other countries.

There is little doubt in my mind that there is a direct causal link between lack of exercise and poor health. I'm sure I'm not alone in believing that the only way out of this vicious circle is going to be based on people increasing their levels of physical exercise.

If a more active life leads to a healthier life, then a more active life should also lead to a happier and more productive life. Taking exercise seriously and accepting a level of responsibility for our personal health has the dual benefits of providing the individual with a better life and reducing our reliance on the NHS.

So, where do we begin? Well, for a start, you could set yourself a simple challenge like walking one mile a week more than you currently walk. Sadly, it's not going to be that easy to convince everyone to walk an extra mile per week, but as individuals we can take on our personal challenges and at least carry out our part in improving the health of our nation.

To really make inroads into getting a significant proportion of the world's population taking more exercise is going to be a complex challenge. It is going to require a large number of initiatives to make it happen. It has already taken up enormous levels of public investment across many nations, but still the trend in how active we are remains stubbornly downwards. Sadly, the trend in public spending on health is increasingly and stubbornly upwards and will have to remain so as long as our willingness to exercise continues on its current descending trajectory.

My starting point for writing this book is that I wanted to write the book I wish I had read when I was 20, and as I read it back to myself now, I feel that I've achieved that goal. Had I read this book in 1980, I might have had a 40-year unbroken run of making a five kilometre journey every day by now, and perhaps enjoyed better health over some of those intervening years. Whatever age you are when you read this book, I just hope that you enjoy it and feel inspired to become more active. You never know, it might make you a healthier, happier, fitter and more confident person. You might even live longer.

While I explore the exercise routines of some exceptionally active and highly driven people, this isn't just about the superfit and hyperactive. This is very much about the busy mum or overweight 60+ year old who makes a deliberate decision to set themselves an apparently simple challenge like getting out and walking a couple of extra miles a week. If you are inspired by their endeavours, or maybe just one of their stories, then that will please me no end. Part 3, which shares the inspiring stories of the people I've spoken to about their exercise challenges, is deliberately very broad in scope. The challenges vary widely, but no matter how big or small, to the people setting those challenges, they represent an incredible effort and great deal of determination.

If you are reading this at the age of 20 or under, then I hope you have many years ahead of you in which you can put these ideas and suggestions into practice. If, on the other hand, you are reading this at a somewhat more mature age, then I would suggest you take the view, "I am the age that I am, and this is my starting point for a new challenge in my life". You are where you are in life, we're all different and at different stages, so take what you can from this book, whoever you are, whatever your age and whatever your starting point.

I'm very much into quick wins, so throughout this book you will find ideas for ways in which you can quickly and simply make a series of effective changes in your life. Before the end of today, go for a walk that you wouldn't have done if you hadn't read this paragraph, or if it is late in the evening just jump up and down on the spot for twenty seconds. If someone sees you doing that they might think you've gone mad, but you will at least have achieved a quick win, and who knows, you might inspire them to jump up and down as well.

The final point I want to make in this Introduction is that when you take some physical exercise, it doesn't just help your physical health, it is also good for your mind and your mental health. I find that it helps me to get away from all the chaos of work and tasks that need to be done and it just calms me down for a while, even if it's just for 15 minutes. I often find that when my brain has a chance to slow down for a few minutes, a bright idea will suddenly pop into my head from out of nowhere. Some of the best lines in this book were composed while I was out walking, running and cycling. In fact, that was one of them. There were many occasions during the writing of this book when I had to rush home from a walk or bike ride to get a really good sentence typed up before it escaped from my short-term memory. In comparison, I only thought of two lines in this book while driving, and that was one of them.

So, go on, give it a go!

PART 1

The Impact of Inactivity on Health and Well-being

1

Finding inspiration and maintaining motivation

When a sportsperson, musician or somebody else in the news is interviewed, they are often asked, "Who was your inspiration?" A common response is the name of a single inspirational figure, but that usually leaves me wondering who their second, third, fourth and thirty-fifth most inspirational figures were.

To get to where we are today we are all inspired, influenced and shaped by a long list of people. The person who had the biggest influence on you wouldn't have provided you with that level of inspiration had it not been for a whole range of other individuals and experiences in your life prior to that.

When Mark Beaumont cycled round the world and Dr Andrew Murray ran from John O'Groats to the Sahara Desert, they inspired me to cycle from Land's End to John O'Groats, but that only happened because Bobby Charlton, Denis Law and George Best inspired me to get outdoors and muddy when I was 7-years-old, and Dave Bedford and

Brendan Foster inspired my passion for running in my early teens, then one of my teachers inspired me to push my limits in cross-country racing and another teacher inspired me to take up hillwalking and climbing, and so it went for the next forty years.

I often wonder who influenced all those people that went on to inspire me, but that tangled web of connections would be incredibly difficult to get to the bottom of, and in any case, that would be looking backwards. Looking forwards, the key aspect of finding inspiration is to be open to being inspired and to receive it and embrace it for all it is worth when it happens. If someone looks like influencing you in a positive way, then listen to them and learn from them, and if this book can inspire you, then read it, absorb it and build up the motivation to make changes in your life.

Inspiring others

In May 2013, I cycled with my partner from Land's End to John O'Groats and we called in to see her work colleagues at their Wednesday morning cake break, which was laid on that day to celebrate our reaching Perthshire. After pigging out on at least ten pieces of cake (I'm not kidding, when you've cycled 800 miles in ten days you develop a massive appetite), I got into discussion with one of Fiona's colleagues. She made a comment that has really stuck with me, "If you can cycle the length of the country, then I should be capable of cycling to work at least a couple of times a week. You've really inspired me to get out of the car and stop being so blooming lazy".

For the first time, I realised that we weren't just being inspired by others, but what we were doing was actually inspiring other people. In her case, as in mine, the person being inspired wasn't copying the person that was inspiring them. That will be a theme of this book and the first of ten principles: "You don't have to copy the person that inspires you. Use your imagination to channel inspiration into your own situation."

Move forward to 2017, and I was fortunate enough to meet Mark Beaumont the day before he set off to Paris to begin his Round the World in 80 Days cycle challenge and mentioned this chain of inspiration to him. His reply was really interesting. He said that stories like that coming back up the chain mean a great deal to him and provide him with the motivation to keep going when he is out there having a really tough day. He's absolutely right, there is something satisfying and reassuring to receive feedback from someone that you've inspired, and in turn, the people that they have gone on to inspire. Don't think of inspiration as being linear and only in one direction, because it is far more complex than that. I would say that it travels in all directions and is most definitely three-dimensional.

There is a crucial element in the process of inspiring and being inspired, and that is communication. If Mark Beaumont cycles round the world, but doesn't tell anyone, then he's only going to inspire a few people who happen to see him on his bike and think, "that reminds me, I must get out and cycle more often". On the other hand, if he writes a book, appears on television, uses social media and gives live presentations around the country, then a wide range of people are going to be inspired in many different ways. Some are going to be inspired to cycle to work, others to undertake their own long journey and maybe someone, somewhere out there, is going to think, "I can go faster than that". Good luck to the person who thinks they can go faster, but the real story is in the great number of people that are inspired to be that bit more active in their daily lives and gain the benefits of better health and well-being as a result.

There have been many great communicators over the years that have written about their adventures and exploits. Like many others, I just need to look along my bookshelves and their names are staring back at me. Many of us have our favourite authors and our own particular sports and activities that we like to read about, but suffice to say that the individuals that have written popular books have told their stories of climbing high mountains or winning Olympic gold medals, and for the majority of us we read those books knowing that we will never climb a mountain of such height or compete at the Olympics, let alone win gold, but their stories are nevertheless exciting. Their stories inspire some of us to go hillwalking or running at our own modest levels, but with renewed enthusiasm.

While there are many great books about sport and adventure, there are also books that are concerned with promoting exercise and good health. This book fits into that latter category. This book is about promoting and celebrating the benefits of regular exercise. It is aimed at exploring the wide spectrum of ways in which people are using their imaginations to increase their participation in exercise, from getting off the bus one stop early in order to get a longer walk to work, through to running every day for over 50 years. Rather than reading about a gold medal performance that, while impressive, you're never likely to emulate, this book includes stories that you should be able to relate to and in some cases maybe even go beyond in terms of distance or level of commitment.

Push and pull - Reactive and proactive

If you ever look back at an improvement that you made in your life, you will often see that there were so called push and pull factors involved in your decision to take some action. When you analyse what happened, there was likely to have been a reason for needing to make that change, pushing you to do something about a particular problem. Your old car kept breaking down and was costing you lots of money in repair bills. The increasingly unreliable car was pushing you to get rid of it and buy a newer vehicle. Then there are the pull factors that draw you towards the answer to your problem. You see a low-mileage car and are motivated to buy it. The old car was pushing you to act and the new car was pulling you to buy it. Push and pull.

Another way of looking at push and pull factors is to think of the kick up the backside as the push, and what you see with your eyes in front of you as the pull.

This chapter on inspiration has so far concentrated on the pull side of the equation. Reading someone's story about their sporting or other kind of success just makes you want to emulate them in some form or other, even if that means running at only half their speed. Their story pulls you towards having a little bit of what they have or do. But what about the push side of exercise? What are the push factors that lead to someone taking more exercise?

Well, I feel that people get the inspiration to take more exercise for a wide range of reasons including to:

1. Lose weight
2. Improve physical health
3. Improve mental health
4. Overcome bereavement
5. Prevent possible future health problems
6. Slow down the ageing process
7. Improve general fitness
8. Improve performance in a particular sport
9. Make new friends and meet people
10. Be more attractive to others, including potential partners.

The top four points in that list can be regarded as reactive and the bottom six as more proactive. If you are overweight and watch a TV documentary on the dangers of carrying too much weight it would be a reactive response to be motivated to take more exercise and strive really hard to lose weight. On the other hand, if you are a healthy weight and watch the same documentary, you might make a proactive decision to take more exercise to reduce your likelihood of putting on weight as you get older and thereby avoid the problems highlighted in the programme.

The reactive stories are always more newsworthy than the proactive ones, but the proactive ones are just as important. The 20-stone man who took up running, went down to 12-stone and ran the London Marathon is a great story that rightly makes it onto TV and radio, as well as into the papers and all over social media, but the woman who avoided putting on weight by walking a mile-a-day is unlikely to attract any media attention. It just isn't an exciting story to tell, and yet it is a brilliant story that should be celebrated and shouted from the rooftops.

You might expect a book like this to be written by someone who used to be overweight or a recovering alcoholic, but (sorry to disappoint if that is what you wanted to read) I'm firmly rooted on the proactive side of the fence. I have always been slim and thankfully have not had any serious health problems, but I have always enjoyed taking exercise and have seen that love of exercise as a proactive way of reducing the risk of weight or health problems in the future.

The theme of reactive and proactive reasons for taking exercise is one that we'll return to later.

So, the push and pull factors are firmly in place and you can work out whether you are in the reactive or proactive camp (or even a bit of both), but where does that spark come from to ignite the passion, and drive someone to take positive action?

Motivational switch

I have taken a question from *The 7 Habits of Highly Effective People* by Stephen R Covey[3] because it is so relevant to this chapter on inspiration and motivation.

I would like you to ask yourself this simple question:

> **What one thing could you do, that you're not doing now, which if done on a regular basis, would make a tremendous positive difference in your personal life?**

Read that question again and have a good think about your answer before you continue reading.

Given that our health underpins everything else we do,

I imagine most people would give an answer relating to an improvement in their health, whether that be their physical or mental health. If you can improve your personal health, you are likely to be increasing the quality of everything else you do in life, such as the time you spend with your family, your performance at work and your ability to think clearly. You are also likely to benefit from a reduction in your reliance on healthcare and medication, and you should just generally feel better in yourself. You may even extend the length of your life.

If you can improve the single most important thing in your life, then surely that must be more important than spending time on things of lower value. If you regard an improvement in your health as the most important thing in your life, then you should view it in that context, be absolutely determined to do something positive about it and drive yourself to succeed.

You are the only person that can get yourself out of the door to go for a walk, so it is up to you to be decisive, make a plan and actually get started. The motivation has to come from within yourself. You have to flick that motivational switch to the ON position.

There are likely to have been hundreds of things you've wanted to do in your life, that have fallen by the wayside because you didn't have time, or lost interest in after a few days, but this one is more important. If you gave an answer to the question above that relates to your health, then doing something positive about it, and sticking at it, has to be far more important than reaching the next level in a game, tidying the shed or watching television.

Your answer to that question should help you form an understanding of why you want to change, and *wanting* to change is vitally important. Wanting to change something is far more important than knowing you should try to change. Wanting to change is a giant first step towards developing the determination to make a change and then actually implementing the change. So, what I would like you to do is imagine yourself in a week's time, a month's time and then a year's time. Imagine you have set yourself a challenge that involves taking more exercise and that you are achieving the target you set yourself. Imagine the positive feeling of your health improving. Even after one week, you are feeling better, and after a month you are even better, and after a year you are better still. Imagine how good you might feel in a year's time and ask yourself if you think you would stop taking exercise at that point and go back to your current lifestyle. I don't think you would. I predict that if you increased your exercise levels for a year and felt the benefits, then you would never go back.

If you go outdoors today and walk a mile, you will have made a start, you will be on the first rung of the ladder and be only six days away from completing your first week. I just encouraged you to think how you would feel after one week. Now, just think how soon you could be in that position and how you could be enjoying those benefits within the next six days, if you make a start today.

Maintaining motivation

Once you have taken decisive action to take more exercise, set yourself a target and actually started getting out there on a regular basis, there is then the challenge of keeping it going. You will need some determination and motivation to keep going when you come to days when, for whatever reason, it isn't easy to get out. That's where friends, family and colleagues can be great motivators. And here's another useful tip: listen to those who encourage and ignore those who mock or discourage.

You will need to focus on your target, make exercise a priority and give yourself a push. Don't let that sentence put you off. This book will provide you with methods and suggestions for giving yourself that push and maintaining your motivation. There are some tricks to doing this, you've already read some of them and you are about to read more.

An interesting quote on inspiration

Before moving onto the next chapter, just pause for a moment to consider this phrase that has been used in a high-profile marketing campaign, "It's not where inspiration comes from, it's where it leads to". By all means be aware of and appreciative of where your inspiration came from but focus on where it is leading to and the positive benefits that you could gain from it.

And here's another one, this time from Roald Dahl:

"I began to realise how important it was to be an enthusiast in life. If you are interested in something, no matter what it is, go at it full speed. Embrace it with both arms, hug it, love it and above all become passionate about it. Lukewarm is no good."

PRINCIPLE NUMBER 1

You don't have to copy the person that inspires you. Use your imagination to channel inspiration into your own situation.

2

Defining obesity

This short chapter provides a description of the term obesity and is included in order for the points raised in Chapter 3 to be more easily understood.

The word *obesity* is used a lot these days, whether it is in the media, medical journals, office chat around the photocopier or pages of this book. So, before going any further, here is an explanation, from the NHS website[4], of what is really meant by the word.

Overview

The word *obese* describes a person who is very overweight, with a lot of body fat.

It's a common problem in the UK that's estimated to affect around one in every four adults and around one in every five children aged 10 to 11.

Defining obesity

There are many ways in which a person's health in relation

to their weight can be classified, but the most widely used method is body mass index (BMI).

BMI is a measure of whether you're a healthy weight for your height. You can use the BMI healthy weight calculator[5] to work out your score.

For most adults, a BMI of:

- 18.5 to 24.9 means you're a healthy weight
- 25 to 29.9 means you're overweight
- 30 to 39.9 means you're obese
- 40 or above means you're severely obese

BMI isn't used to definitively diagnose obesity, because people who are very muscular sometimes have a high BMI without excess fat. But for most people, BMI is a useful indication of whether they're a healthy weight, overweight or obese.

A better measure of excess fat is waist circumference, which can be used as an additional measure in people who are overweight (with a BMI of 25 to 29.9) or moderately obese (with a BMI of 30 to 34.9).

Generally, men with a waist circumference of 94 centimetres (37 inches) or more and women with a waist circumference of 80 centimetres (about 31.5 inches) or more are more likely to develop obesity-related health problems.

The scale of the obesity problem is highlighted graphically in the Public Health England diagram shown overleaf[6, 7].

Find Time for Exercise

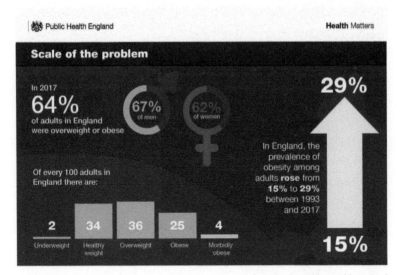

Infographic by Public Health England

3

The mind-boggling scale of the problem

The facts, figures, statistics, expert opinions and projections surrounding the impacts of lack of exercise on the world's health are truly alarming. Indeed, the figures you are about to read in this chapter are staggering, to an eye-watering degree. Try to get your head around the following statements and statistics:

- Estimates suggested that obesity cost the NHS £5.1 billion in 2006/07[8]. This was more than the £3.3 billion attributed to smoking-related ill health and £3.3 billion attributed to alcohol-related ill health. In addition, obesity cost social care a further £352 million in extra hours of help.
- By 2019[9], the estimated cost of obesity to the NHS was £6.1 billion, a rise of £1 billion in 12 years. Furthermore, the cost to wider society is now estimated to be £27 billion.

- According to Public Health England[8], physical inactivity is responsible for 1 in 6 deaths in the UK, making it as dangerous as smoking, but over 1 in 4 of us take less than 30 minutes of physical exercise each week.
- According to estimates from Public Health England[8], two thirds of adults and a quarter of children between two and ten years old are overweight or obese. Obese children are more likely to become overweight adults and to suffer premature ill health and mortality and, by 2034, 70 per cent of adults are expected to be overweight or obese.
- One in ten over 40s now has type 2 diabetes, and the number of people living with all types of diabetes has reached 4.7 million in the UK. The number of people affected by diabetes is expected to reach 5.5 million by 2030[10].

It is not surprising that governments are concerned by figures like these, so in 2007 the Government Office for Science published the Foresight project report, *Tackling Obesities: Future Choices*[11], which used scientific evidence, commissioned research and expert advice to look forward 40 years, estimate the likely figures around the year 2050 and take a strategic view of the issue of obesity. The following quote from the report highlights the estimated scale of the problem by 2050.

"In recent years Britain has become a nation where overweight is the norm. The rate of increase in overweight and obesity, in children and adults, is striking. By 2050, Foresight modelling indicates that 60% of adult men, 50% of adult women and about 25% of all children under 16 could be obese. Obesity increases the risk of a range of chronic diseases, particularly type 2 diabetes, stroke and coronary heart disease and also cancer and arthritis. The NHS costs attributable to overweight and obesity are projected to double to £10 billion per year by 2050. The wider costs to society and business are estimated to reach £49.9 billion per year (at today's prices)."

International comparisons

This issue is a worldwide one and it is worth considering the scale of the problem across the world and where the UK ranks against other nations. These statistics are taken from the NHS England publication, *Adult obesity international comparisons data factsheet*[12]:

- Worldwide in 2014, more than 1.9 billion adults (18 years and older) were overweight. Of these, over 600 million were obese, representing 13% of the total adult population. The current world population is estimated to be around 7.4 billion.
- The UK ranks 8th for overweight prevalence (including obesity) for men and women combined, out of the 34 Organisation for Economic Cooperation and Development (OECD) countries.
- The UK ranks 8th for overweight prevalence (including obesity) in men (66.6%) and 7th for women (57.2%), out of the 34 OECD countries.
- The UK ranks 5th for obesity prevalence among men (24.5%) and 10th for women (25.4%), out of the 34 OECD countries.
- The US ranks 1st for obesity prevalence among men

(31.7%) and 2nd for women (33.9%), out of the 34 OECD countries. Turkey has the highest prevalence of obesity among women at 34.1%.

- Japan has the lowest prevalence of obesity among men (4.5%) and women (3.3%) as well as the lowest prevalence of overweight (including obesity) for both men (28.9%) and women (17.6%).

- Trends over 30 years show that overweight prevalence (including obesity) in England is consistently lower than in the US. However, the rate of increase is higher. Overweight levels in England have increased by 72% from 36.0% in 1980 to 62.1% in 2013, compared to a 46% increase in the US over the same time period.

Note that some caution is needed when comparing obesity prevalence internationally as there can be differences in data collection methods, timing and frequency of surveys.

The trend is spiraling downwards

Not only is the scale of this problem so bleak – it is getting worse at an alarming rate. The following figures are from a report produced for the NHS in 2013, titled *Statistics on Obesity, Physical Activity and Diet: England, 2013*[13]. These figures refer to research carried out in England and compare data collected in 1993 and 2011. The changes observed over this 18-year period are quite sobering:

- The proportion of adults with a normal BMI decreased between 1993 and 2011 from 41% to 34% among men and from 50% to 39% among women.

- The proportion that were overweight, including obese, increased from 58% to 65% in men and from 49% to 58% in women between 1993 and 2011.
- There was a marked increase in the proportion of adults that were obese from 13% in 1993 to 24% in 2011 for men and from 16% to 26% for women.

Consequences of obesity

One possible consequence of this upward trend in overweight and obesity rates has been a decline in average life expectancy rates. For centuries, there has been an ongoing and steady rise in the mean average length of a human life span. Apart from a few temporary downward blips caused by war and pandemics, the trend has been on a long-term rise. However, in recent years, researchers have noticed the beginning of a downward trend, with average life expectancies coming down. This has led to predictions that for young people growing up today, their life expectancy could be less than that for their parents. Given the advances in medical care that led to the impressive rise in life expectancy rates, and the further advances that are still being made at the current time, it is deeply depressing that unhealthy habits could be responsible for average life expectancy to be falling.

Simon Stevens, Chief Executive of NHS England is reported as saying, "Obesity is the new smoking. It is a slow-motion car crash in terms of avoidable illness and rising health care costs"[14].

As for the financial consequences of obesity for the NHS, Simon Stevens went on to say, "If as a nation we keep piling on the pounds around the waistline, we'll be piling on the pounds in terms of future taxes needed just to keep the NHS afloat".

Obesity increases the risk of a number of health issues, including heart disease, diabetes, musculoskeletal disorders, cancers, depression and anxiety. Severely obese individuals are three times more likely to require social care than those with a normal weight, resulting in increased risk of hospitalisation and associated health and social care costs.

While this book is primarily about promoting regular physical activity to improve an individual's physical and mental health, I do acknowledge that there are other medical reasons for a wide range of conditions including obesity, and that exercise alone is not the solution to everyone's health-related problem. An increase in daily levels of physical exercise cannot fix everyone's problems, but adopted as part of a balanced lifestyle, most crucially including improvements in diet, exercise has the potential to make a significant contribution towards the future well-being of most people. The key to tackling obesity, therefore, is usually a combination of better diet and more exercise.

Mental health

The health issues that are creating such a heavy burden on our NHS aren't just confined to physical health problems. Mental health is also a major issue and the figures are just as alarming as they are for physical health problems:

- It is estimated that 1 in 4 of us experience a mental health problem every year[15].
- Common mental health problems such as depression and

anxiety are distributed according to a gradient of economic disadvantage across society. The poorer and more disadvantaged are disproportionately affected by common mental health problems and their adverse consequences[16].

- Mixed anxiety and depression have been estimated to cause one-fifth of days lost from work in Britain[16].

Paying to correct the problem

This may be an obvious statement, but our taxes pay for our NHS – so the unhealthier we are as a nation, the more we need to work, to raise the taxes, to pay for the service. However, if the health of the nation were to improve, the burden on us to raise the necessary funding would start to come down. There is, therefore, a direct link between the collective health of the nation and the amount of money that needs to be channelled from our taxes into the NHS.

Hope from amongst the disaster

It would be possible to fill a book the size of *War and Peace* with facts, figures and statistics to support the argument that physical and mental health problems represent a major challenge facing the modern world. What I have presented above is just a snapshot, a thought-provoking summary, of the mind-boggling scale of the problem.

However, there is hope, and that hope comes in the form of exercise, because **regular physical exercise can address both physical and mental health issues, and it can be used as prevention and treatment. It treats the whole person.** If you think of regular exercise as a form of medication, then what you have is **an intervention that can target both physical and mental health, and be used as a form of prevention as well as treatment. It treats the whole person.**

I have deliberately repeated that phrase (and highlighted it in bold text), because it is so important, so pivotal to the reasoning being presented in this book.

	Physical	Mental
Prevention	✓	✓
Treatment	✓	✓

Exercise can be used to treat and prevent physical and mental health problems. That has to be a pretty resounding argument in favour of promoting its wide-ranging benefits.

A long-term strategy

Returning to the Foresight project. The conclusions in that report made the following recommendations:

"This Foresight project has taken a strategic 40-year forward look at how society could respond sustainably to obesity:

- Most adults in the UK are already overweight. Modern living ensures every generation is heavier than the last – 'Passive Obesity'.
- By 2050, 60% of men and 50% of women could be clinically obese. Without action, obesity-related diseases are estimated to cost society £49.9 billion per year.
- The obesity epidemic cannot be prevented by individual action alone and demands a societal approach.

- Tackling obesity requires far greater change than anything tried so far, and at multiple levels: personal, family, community and national.
- Preventing obesity is a societal challenge, similar to climate change. It requires partnership between government, science, business and civil society."

While this book is promoting individual action, I have to agree wholeheartedly with the third bullet point in that list – the obesity epidemic cannot be prevented by individual action alone and demands a societal approach. Nevertheless, individual actions can and do lead to healthier and more fulfilling lives for those who decide to take more exercise and that can also contribute towards a reduction in that individual's burden on the NHS. Furthermore, the actions of an individual can influence other family members and people within their communities, and that groundswell of more and more people taking individual action can eventually make a difference at a national level.

The solution needs to be a mixture of bottom-up and top-down approaches. Initiatives to encourage individual actions represent the bottom-up, or individual-level approach, and this book sets out to be a part of that bottom-up movement, but there does need to be a corresponding, strong and effective top-down, population-level approach as well, and this will be discussed later.

The final bullet point rightly draws a comparison with climate change. I would argue that along with climate change and plastic pollution, obesity and human physical inactivity combine to be one of the most pressing and urgent societal challenges that we face today. As the Foresight project report concludes, it is going to require partnership between government, science, business and civil society.

It really is time for everyone, every individual, you, me and politicians to take this issue seriously and take action to be a part of the solution rather than a part of the problem.

4

The chair

If you're a fruit picker, plasterer, ski instructor, lumberjack or lumberjill then this won't describe your typical day, but for many others, this may sound all too familiar:

- Wake up to the alarm feeling you haven't had sufficient sleep.
- Get out of bed, wander through to the bathroom and sit on the toilet.
- Clean your teeth and step into the shower.
- Sit down to have breakfast.
- Sit in the car, bus or train and go to work.
- Walk a short distance to the office and sit down at your desk to check emails.
- Remain sitting for the morning session at work.
- Stop for your lunch break, where you sit down to eat a sandwich, biscuit and, if you're health conscious, piece of fruit.
- Go back to your desk (assuming you actually left your desk) for your afternoon session of sitting down looking at a computer screen.
- Attend a mid-afternoon meeting at which you sit round a

table with several of your colleagues before going back to your desk for the final hour of the working day.

- Switch off your computer, walk to your car, bus stop or railway station and go home.
- Stand at the chopping board, cooker and/or microwave to make your evening meal.
- Sit down to eat your meal.
- Retire to the settee (assuming you had your meal at the table) for three hours to watch television.
- Stagger upstairs to the bathroom to clean your teeth.
- Get into bed and lie down for seven hours of insufficient sleep.
- Repeat for several decades.

Does that sound all too familiar to you?

Look how many of those bullet points in your typical day involved sitting down.

The only one that included the word *stand* was in the cooking an evening meal category. The teeth cleaning ones also involve standing but, eh, let's not get too excited about the four-minutes of daily exercise involved in that activity. Well, actually, wait until you get to Chapter 27: *Suggested routines*, and you might just have a reason for getting mildly excited about the four-minutes of daily activity while cleaning your teeth.

The only two that included the word *walk* were walking from your transport to office in the morning and the return journey in the afternoon. If that sums up your journey to and from your desk, how far is that walk and, if you drive, how determined are you to keep that distance to an absolute minimum?

To me, the words that really leap out of that list are sit, desk, screen, meeting, settee and bed. Admittedly we all have to lie down in bed and get some sleep, but the amount of time we spend sitting, driving and staring at a screen is pretty scary. A recent poll[17] estimated that many office workers are now spending 1,700 hours a year in front of a computer screen.

The chair, in its many formats (car seat, office chair, dining chair and settee), is the crux of the problem. I'll not include toilet seat in that list – we all need to go.

The chair really has become the grim reaper's new weapon of mass destruction. It's time to recognise that fact and commit to doing something about it. It's time to fight back, punch your right fist high in the air, rise off the settee in revolt and stomp away from the computer screen. It's time for us all to question how much time we spend on our backsides and take some positive action to sit less, stand more and move more.

All chairs should have a warning sign nailed to them, front and back, and these signs should be so big, so prominent, that we could not approach a chair without seeing the writing on these signs.

WARNING

This is a chair. It is potentially hazardous to your health, could shorten your life, and in conjunction with other chairs has the potential to bankrupt the country. Use sparingly and only for short periods of less than half an hour in one sitting.

Sit Less – Stand More – Move More

The health impacts from sitting

If the chair is so bad for us, what exactly is it that happens to us when we sit down?

The main health problem associated with excessive sitting is a decrease in electrical activity in the leg muscles. So why, I hear you asking, is that so bad? Well, electrical activity is a measurement of nerve and muscle activity, and sitting causes that activity in your legs and butt muscles to switch off.

The follow-on to that is that calorie burning drops to almost one per minute, or 68 per hour. Standing for an hour would increase that rate to around 100 calories per hour. Walk and that rate goes up further to around 230 or 240. The next impact in this chain reaction is that enzymes that help break down fat drop by a massive 90% when you are sitting[18].

So, basically, our legs are going numb through lack of movement, we're burning fewer calories and we're losing the ability to burn fat. You can see where all of this is leading, and it's not good. Weight gain.

For many of us, sitting eight hours a day at our jobs is inevitable, but it's the extra sitting outside of work that turns a serious problem into a far deadlier one. It's bad enough to sit all day at work, but to sit all evening at home just adds to the damage.

Moving around during the day, getting up from the desk and having a daily exercise routine, are all ways of keeping those nerves and muscles awake and functioning properly. We might use phrases like *comfortable chair* and *cushy sofa*, but we need to learn to view these things as the nasty, evil, serial killers they have become.

We need to interrupt our periods of sitting whenever possible. We also need to be aware that movement pumps more blood and oxygen through the brain, whereas sitting slows everything down, including our brain function. The irony of that is that sitting-down jobs are usually associated with the need to think, but sitting is linked with impairment of the ability to think. The conclusion to be drawn here is that you will perform your chair-based job better if you stand up and walk away from your desk on a regular basis. Yes, that does mean taking time out from your task in hand to leave your desk for a while, but you will be more effective when you are at your desk.

Here's a head-to-toe look at what the act of prolonged sitting can do to our bodies:

Head, neck and shoulders	**Brain function** During exercise, our muscles work harder and fresh, oxygenated blood is pumped to our brain, triggering the release of natural chemicals, such as endorphins, which can create a positive feeling in the body. Prolonged sitting causes our bodily systems, including brain function, to slow down.
	Stiff neck Sitting at a computer often leads to a stiff neck due to us holding our head and neck at an unnatural angle to look at the keyboard and screen.
	Tired shoulders Poor head and neck posture creates tension in our shoulder and upper back muscles. Typing adds to these problems due to our shoulders supporting outstretched arms.
Major organs	**Heart disease** When we sit, our muscles burn less fat and blood flow becomes sluggish. Slow-moving fat in our arteries can result in them becoming clogged, leading to increased risks of heart attacks and strokes, as well as other problems such as elevated cholesterol and high blood pressure. Exercise, on the other hand, has the potential to strengthen the heart.

	Lungs If we avoid activities that make us breathless, our muscles become weaker. Weaker muscles need more oxygen to work. Over time we feel more and more breathless. This is called the cycle of inactivity, or cycle of breathlessness.	
	Over-productive pancreas The pancreas produces hormones, particularly insulin, that control blood glucose levels. Sitting can interfere with the ability of the cells in our muscles to respond appropriately to insulin; this can cause the pancreas to go into over-production, leading to diabetes.	
	Cancer of the major organs Inactivity, including sitting, is often linked with an increased risk of colorectal, ovarian, breast and endometrial cancers. Regular exercise is believed to boost production of antioxidants, our defence mechanism against cell-damaging and potentially cancer-causing free radicals.	
Spine	**Disc damage** Exercise enables the soft discs between vertebrae to expand and contract, and absorb fresh blood and nutrients. Sitting has the opposite effect of compressing the discs, thereby increasing the risk of uneven squashing and herniated discs.	
	Back pain Prolonged sitting often leads to stiff and painful back conditions due to a combination of disc damage, trapped nerves, and tight muscles, tendons and ligaments caused by poor posture and lack of movement.	
Muscles	**Abdominals** Abdominal muscles work to keep us upright when we are standing or sitting straight up, but as soon as we sit back they go unused. Weak abdominals, tight back muscles and an under-used psoas muscle (linking the spine with our legs) combine to pull the lower spine forward.	
	Hip flexors The right angle created at our hips during sitting leads to a shortening of the hip flexors. These muscles, at the top of our thighs, become tight through lack of extension, thereby losing their ability to flex properly. Tight hip flexors fail to provide the support and balance we need, and our stride length can become limited.	

	Inglorious glutes The gluteal muscles of the buttocks help move the hip joint and stabilise the pelvis to maintain posture and balance. Sitting provides these muscles with no real work to do, apart from getting squashed, and the result can be soft, flabby, inglorious glutes incapable of performing their vital roles. Exercise is the key to having glorious glutes.
Legs	**Weak bones** The bones in our hips and legs need weight-bearing activities like walking and running in order to maintain their density and strength. The rise in cases of osteoporosis may be linked to prolonged sitting.
	Slow circulation Prolonged sitting results in blood circulation slowing, which in turn causes fluids to pool in our lower legs. This can result in swollen ankles, varicose veins and deep vein thrombosis.

PRINCIPLE NUMBER 2

Sit less –
Stand more –
Move more.

5

Escaping the physical inactivity crisis

Whenever a television news item addresses the issue of exercise being a solution to the nation's health crisis, or even the physical inactivity pandemic, the accompanying film is usually of skimpily clad young people in a gym. Middle-aged or older people taking a brisk walk in a park or out in the countryside would, in my view, be more appropriate to the story, but time-after-time the stock images of exercise bikes and treadmills in a gym are used as the example of how we could exercise our way out of this health crisis. I often wonder how many people are put off by the pictures of a gym, which costs money, requires specialist clothing and involves a certain amount of time and effort to get to and from.

The simplicity of walking would be a far more appropriate image to show. You can do it straight from your door, you only need a short time slot in your day, you can leave your wallet at home and you don't even need to get changed. There are many ways to exercise the human body and provide it with the associated health benefits, so it would be great to see that range of options being reflected in the kind of news stories that are aired on a regular basis.

If the makers of these television news items and documentaries are reading this, can I request that you at least balance the gym images with a few shots of older people, wrapped up in a few layers of warm clothing and enjoying a brisk walk, please? If we are to win this "battle of the bulge," as the media often describe it, then our paths and pavements are likely to play at least as great a role as the treadmills and rowing machines.

That is not to say that gyms don't have their place in this world. They certainly do. For many sportspeople they are the place where the foundations of strength are laid for improving performance, whether that be on the running track, football pitch or other sporting venue. For many others, a gym is a great place to exercise and enjoy some valuable social interaction with friends. I've spent many a muscle-stretching hour in gyms and enjoyed sweating my way to some kind of fitness, so I'm not going to knock them. What I am saying, however, is that I don't think they should be portrayed as the backdrop to every opportunity to demonstrate people taking exercise. There are many ways to take exercise and it should be borne in mind that many people don't like gyms, indeed many people don't like sport, but there are still forms of exercise that they can enjoy, and it would be helpful if that was recognised and taken account of when addressing this issue in the media, especially on television.

Given that this issue is of concern to all of us, whatever our age, then it is important that encouragement and investment go into promoting the health benefits of a wide range of exercise types to both genders and people of all ages.

Turn to face the good magnets

Like millions of people around the world, I was enthralled by the 2012 London Olympics and Paralympics, and the 2014 Commonwealth Games in Glasgow, and believe passionately in the push for there to be a legacy from those games.

If major sporting events like the Olympics and Commonwealth Games are to have a lasting and meaningful legacy, then there needs to be a balance between encouraging young people into sport and investment in the promotion of exercise for people of all ages and backgrounds. If events of that kind can play their part in addressing the scourge of inactivity, then they will be making a very worthwhile contribution to one of the most urgent issues facing the modern world.

The UK government invests millions of pounds in funding Olympic and Paralympic athletes with a view to winning medals and propelling Team GB up the medal tables. The good news, from a British point of view, is that it has worked. In the 1996 Summer Olympics in Atlanta, we finished in 36th place in the table with one gold medal, eight silver and six bronze. By 2016 in Rio de Janeiro, and following a significant rise in investment as a result of the National Lottery, we had climbed up to second in the table, behind the USA and ahead of China, with 27 gold, 23 silver and 17 bronze. By any stretch of the imagination, that is a fantastic achievement.

One of the justifications for this funding of elite sport is that medals and Olympic success will rub off and lead to an increase in sporting activity amongst the general population. Assessments of the long-term legacy from investment in elite sports vary widely, with some reports claiming there is evidence that enthusiasm for the Olympics is not having the desired effect of getting us active in sufficient numbers. My view on this is that I think Olympic success is having a positive impact in terms of getting more people more active, it's just that the most noticeable group of people being enthused by it are those who are already most active. People like me, and many others who are members of running clubs, cycling clubs and a whole host of other sports clubs were so inspired by the Games, we became even more active than before.

Olympic success is like a magnet pulling in a positive direction. That positively charged magnet is made up of all the factors that encourage people to take part in sport and physical activity. So, as well as Olympic medals, it also includes school sport, parkrun, posters and leaflets in doctors' surgeries, self-help books, lifestyle magazines and many other factors that encourage an active lifestyle.

However, according to Newton's Third Law of Motion, for every action, there is an equal and opposite reaction, and this appears to be the case with the promotion of physical activity. Pulling in the negative direction, in opposition to medals, parkruns and health campaigns, are the long list of causes of our current health crisis: inactivity, desk-based working, hectic lifestyles, smoking, junk food and so on.

With two sets of forces pulling in opposite directions like this, it is easy to see how an individual can be drawn towards one or other of the magnets. Whenever I consider this issue, I feel that an individual is more likely to be drawn towards the magnet closest to them. In other words, if you are already active and inclined to look after your personal health, you are more likely to be inspired by watching Team

GB winning gold medals and receptive to the information contained in a leaflet that you pick up at your doctor's surgery.

In contrast to that scenario, a person who is inactive and less concerned about their health is more likely to see Olympic success as entertainment, rather than inspiration, and a health promotion leaflet as a message from Big Brother, rather than helpful advice. Sadly, it would appear that the forces exerted by the negative magnets are just too powerful for some and it can feel like there is an inevitability about being drawn in that direction. I will return to that word *inevitability* towards the end of this chapter.

There will be people somewhere in the middle that lead inactive lives and have a moderately poor diet, who for whatever reason begin to take modest amounts of exercise, and that is to be celebrated and encouraged. But a possible outcome of the two magnets analogy I'm describing is one where we become increasingly polarised with more and more people being drawn towards one or other end of the spectrum, with fewer and fewer left in the middle. Over time, it feels like the fit are getting fitter and the inactive are becoming increasingly inactive. If that is the case, then I can't help feeling that it's time to strengthen the positive magnets. It is time to turn and face the good magnets.

The International Olympic Committee, national governments, government agencies, host cities, sporting bodies and charitable organisations are devoting substantial resources to strengthening those positive magnets, so when reports emerge suggesting they're not having the desired effect, that should not be the signal to throw in the towel and give up, but to re-double their commitment and efforts.

Time spent in nature

Talking of good magnets, to my mind there is no better magnet to get me outdoors than the pure joy of being out in nature. I subscribe to the adage, "Time spent in nature is time well spent". Whether you are into gentle walks in a local wood or running up mountains, the healing properties of just being outdoors in the fresh air are a wonderful accompaniment to the exercise you happen to be taking.

There is a theory that humans have a natural urge to affiliate with other forms of life. The word *biophilia* refers to our need to be close to other life forms and stay as close as possible to nature. Most people would prefer, and respond better to, a view out of a window that looks onto a tree than a view of a brick wall. As well as the obvious air quality issues, most people would prefer a walk in a forest or urban park to a congested city street, because there is a simple pleasure in being close to trees, plants, water and animals that satisfies a basic human need to connect with nature.

Amongst the many changes I feel we need to make in order to incrementally turn around this health crisis and battle with obesity and mental health issues, is going to be some kind of re-connection between the people and the outdoor world. The UK needs its version of the Scandinavian cultural philosophy of *friluftsliv* (literally: free-air-life) because all people, given the opportunity, have a natural tendency to connect with nature.

People that are well connected with their outdoor environment are more likely to be confident there, show greater environmental respect and gain more pleasure and wider health benefits from their time spent outdoors. Having rights and responsibilities, developing a bond with our outdoor environment, and enjoying the associated health benefits are vitally important to a society and form the basis of making a valuable contribution towards solving our inactivity crisis.

The environmental journalist George Monbiot is critical of the current education system and advocates a greater role for outdoor education in order to create a much stronger connection between young people and the outdoor world. In his article *Housebroken*[19] he makes this statement in support of children being better connected with nature in order for them to gain personal benefits from it and, in turn, to be better informed and more likely to want to defend nature:

> *"Forest Schools, Outward Bound, Woodcraft Folk, the John Muir Award, the Campaign for Adventure, Natural Connections, family nature clubs and many others are trying to bring children and the natural world back together again. But all of them are fighting forces which, if they cannot be turned, will strip the living planet of the wonder and delight, of the ecstacy that for millennia have drawn children into the wilds."*

Time spent in nature is always well spent. Whether it is deep in the mountains or amongst the trees in a city park, nature is a fantastic resource, a wonderful accompaniment to physical activity and just a great healer. I, for one, just can't get enough of being out in nature, and if you look back to the Foreword by Sean Conway, it is worth noting that one of his three golden rules is to spend more time outside in natural light. Don't underestimate the health benefits[20] of the vitamin

D our bodies create from safe levels of exposure to sunlight during the summer months.

Health benefits and the ageing process

Another observation is the high proportion of people that seem to slip from being young and reasonably fit to older and inactive as they reach their middle years. This would appear to be another case for requiring a more powerful positive magnet to counteract the forces from the other direction. The challenge to keep those who are active in their twenties and thirties remaining active through the second half of their working lives is one that society shouldn't give up on. Work and family life may become busier and more stressful, but to let exercise get squeezed out of your life is to allow physical and mental health problems to get a foot in your door.

If you are at least reasonably active and reading this in your twenties, you can look forward and make a plan to ensure you stay active. If you are inactive and in your forties, fifties or beyond, then you can still think positively and make a plan; after all, it is never too late to become more active. As I stated earlier, you are where you are. You are the age, weight and body shape that you are. This is your starting point. This is reality.

The following passage is taken from the Mental Health Foundation publication, *How to look after your mental health using exercise*[21], and makes the case perfectly clearly that physical activity is of great benefit to older people:

> *"Improvements in healthcare have led to an increasing life expectancy and a growing population of people over*

65 years. Alongside this increase in life expectancy, there has been an increase in the number of people living with dementia and in people with cognitive decline. The main symptom of dementia is memory loss; it is a progressive disease that results in people becoming more impaired over time. Decline in cognitive functions, such as attention and concentration, also occurs in older people, including those who do not develop dementia. Physical activity has been identified as a protective factor in studies that examined risk factors for dementia. For people who have already developed the disease, physical activity can help to delay further decline in functioning. Studies show that there is approximately a 20% to 30% lower risk of depression and dementia for adults participating in daily physical activity. Physical activity also seems to reduce the likelihood of experiencing cognitive decline in people who do not have dementia."

Avoiding barriers

At a time when we are facing a crisis that has been created by reduced levels of exercise, it saddens me when I see barriers being placed in the way of people taking much needed exercise. In 1996, a Scottish Office Minister actually suggested in a speech that people could be charged a fee for walking on mountains. His idea was widely criticised and the suggestion was never repeated. Much of that criticism was centred on the claim that what he was proposing was a tax on exercise. Likewise, the actions of Stoke Gifford Council that wanted to charge people for taking part in the Little Stoke parkrun, which would have gone against the parkrun ethos of always being free to enter, was also seen by many as an attempt to tax exercise. The last thing we should be doing right now is placing barriers of that kind in the way of people that desperately need to take more exercise.

It is entirely correct that hillwalkers make contributions towards the cost of path repair works and that runners make donations to parkrun and purchase parkrun products, but to set a mandatory charge for a walk on a hill or parkrun event would be to deny those that can't afford it, and therefore quite likely the ones who need it most. It would mainly exclude the young, for whom a charge could not only prevent them from participating now, but also prevent their future participation because they never get into the activity when they are young. And then there are the elderly, who might not have the spare cash they enjoyed when they were working.

Inevitability

I said I would return to that word *inevitability*. There shouldn't be any kind of inevitability about anyone being drawn by the negative magnets into an unhealthy life without exercise. There are some truly inspirational examples of people that seemed destined to an inevitable life of poor physical or mental health, but who turned things around because somehow, through whatever circumstances, they discovered the attraction of a positive magnet.

Change

If we are to avoid the obesity rates that were predicted by the Foresight project, then something is going to have to change, and if we are to turn around all the other health-related issues that I've discussed in Part 1 of this book, then the kind of change we need is not just going to be a bit of tinkering around the edges, it is going to have to be truly monumental.

Whenever massive change is required, we tend to look to national governments and international organisations to introduce policies and funding commitments to make the transition happen. The result is that we might sit back and wait for government to act, or we might be motivated to go out and protest in order to influence the change that we wish to see. After all, the individual can feel small and insignificant when, for example, it comes to wanting the government of the day to take on the might of some big business interest that is perceived to be doing something bad.

However, when it comes to health, obesity and exercise, there is an amazingly simple reason for starting one person at a time. As soon as you start taking more exercise, you are reducing your risks of contracting certain illnesses, increasing your chances of a longer and happier life, and reducing your burden on the NHS.

If this almighty problem is to be tackled successfully, then it is going to be a combination of change at the personal level, with millions of individuals increasing their time being active, and at the political level with policies and legislation to improve the quality of our food and drink, plus funding to make it easier for us to get involved in healthy forms of exercise.

The drive to tackle this issue on a worldwide scale is being led by the World Health Organization (WHO), and a great example of a WHO international initiative is the Global Action Plan on Physical Activity 2018 to 2030[22]. This Action

Plan sets a target of reducing physical inactivity by 15% by 2030, and outlines 20 recommended policy actions and interventions that are universally applicable to all countries.

The WHO supports all countries in the development of their responses to this crisis and that work results in the Chief Medical Officers' Physical Activity Guidelines in the UK, and equivalent policy documents in nearly every country around the world.

In 2020, the WHO published its Guidelines on Physical Activity and Sedentary Behaviour[23]. These updated guidelines are based on a much larger scientific evidence base than the previous 2010 guidelines, so now include evidence for additional health benefits from physical activity, specific recommendations for pregnant and post-partum women and for people living with chronic conditions and disabilities.

The previous requirement from the 2010 guidelines for 10-minute minimum duration of continuous activity has been dropped in favour of "some physical activity is better than none". The headline phrase now is *Every Move Counts*.

It is reassuring that a great deal of vital work is being carried out by some very dedicated people, all around the world, to develop initiatives aimed at tackling this monumental problem of inactivity. The way that the WHO is leading from the top is to be highly commended.

Having said that, the focus in this book is very much on finding ways to increase exercise at the personal level, but that is not in any way a signal that governments should be let off the hook. Far from it.

6

The positive impacts of exercise

Having looked at the negative impacts of inactivity, let's take a moment to appreciate the main health benefits of regular physical activity as highlighted in this Public Health England diagram[24, 7].

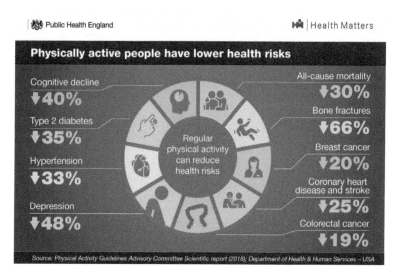

Infographic by Public Health England

Find Time for Exercise

In addition to those headline benefits, physical exercise can also have the following list of additional benefits:

Reduce stress and anxiety	Exercise is known to alleviate the symptoms of stress and anxiety as a result of releasing natural chemicals such as endorphins and norepinephrine. This in turn aids relaxation and the ability to sleep.
Boost brainpower	Cardiovascular or aerobic exercise that gets your heart to work harder and pump blood around your body helps to strengthen your heart, and the extra flow of blood to the brain helps boost its power and efficiency. This also has the effect of sharpening memory.
Improve productivity	Studies have shown that people that find time for exercise on a regular basis are more productive, less sleepy and have more energy than their more sedentary peers.
Improve self-confidence	Physical exercise can boost self-esteem leading to an improvement in self-image and overall benefits for mental health.
Production of vitamin D	Exposure to sunlight in the outdoors (while using sunscreen) enables our bodies to produce vitamin D, which can boost the immune system and reduce depression.

7

Chief Medical Officers' Guidelines

Guidelines issued by the Chief Medical Officers (CMOs) of England, Scotland, Wales and Northern Ireland in 2019 are contained in the UK Chief Medical Officers' Physical Activity Guidelines[25&7] and emphasise the importance of physical activity for people of all ages through following a life course approach.

Summary of Guidelines by age group

Under-5s
Infants (less than 1 year):

- Infants should be physically active several times every day in a variety of ways, including interactive floor-based activity, e.g. crawling.
- For infants not yet mobile, this includes at least 30 minutes of tummy time spread throughout the day while awake (and other movements such as reaching and grasping, pushing and pulling themselves independently, or rolling over); more is better.

NB: Tummy time may be unfamiliar to babies at first, but can be increased gradually, starting from a minute or two at a time, as the baby becomes used to it. Babies should not sleep on their tummies.

Toddlers (1-2 years):
- Toddlers should spend at least 180 minutes (3 hours) per day in a variety of physical activities at any intensity, including active and outdoor play, spread throughout the day; more is better.

Pre-schoolers (3-4 years):
- Pre-schoolers should spend at least 180 minutes (3 hours) per day in a variety of physical activities spread throughout the day, including active and outdoor play. More is better; the 180 minutes should include at least 60 minutes of moderate-to-vigorous intensity physical activity.

Children and Young People (5 to 18 years)
- Children and young people should engage in moderate-to-vigorous intensity physical activity for an average of at least 60 minutes per day across the week. This can include all forms of activity such as physical education, active travel, after-school activities, play and sports.
- Children and young people should engage in a variety of types and intensities of physical activity across the week to develop movement skills, muscular fitness, and bone strength.
- Children and young people should aim to minimise the amount of time spent being sedentary, and when

physically possible should break up long periods of not moving with at least light physical activity.

Adults (19 to 64 years)

- For good physical and mental health, adults should aim to be physically active every day. Any activity is better than none, and more is better still.
- Adults should do activities to develop or maintain strength in the major muscle groups. These could include heavy gardening, carrying heavy shopping, or resistance exercise. Muscle strengthening activities should be done on at least two days a week, but any strengthening activity is better than none.
- Each week, adults should accumulate at least 150 minutes (2½ hours) of moderate intensity activity (such as brisk walking or cycling); or 75 minutes of vigorous intensity activity (such as running); or even shorter durations of very vigorous intensity activity (such as sprinting or stair climbing); or a combination of moderate, vigorous and very vigorous intensity activity.
- Adults should aim to minimise the amount of time spent being sedentary, and when physically possible should break up long periods of inactivity with at least light physical activity.

Older Adults (65 years and over)

- Older adults should participate in daily physical activity to gain health benefits, including maintenance of good physical and mental health, wellbeing, and social functioning. Some physical activity is better than none: even light activity brings some health benefits compared to being sedentary, while more daily physical activity provides greater health and social benefits.

- Older adults should maintain or improve their physical function by undertaking activities aimed at improving or maintaining muscle strength, balance and flexibility on at least two days a week. These could be combined with sessions involving moderate aerobic activity or could be additional sessions aimed specifically at these components of fitness.

- Each week older adults should aim to accumulate 150 minutes (2½ hours) of moderate intensity aerobic activity, building up gradually from current levels. Those who are already regularly active can achieve these benefits through 75 minutes of vigorous intensity activity, or a combination of moderate and vigorous activity, to achieve greater benefits. Weight-bearing activities which create an impact through the body help to maintain bone health.

- Older adults should break up prolonged periods of being sedentary with light activity when physically possible, or at least with standing, as this has distinct health benefits for older people.

PART 2

My Challenge

8

The five kilometres
per day challenge

In the spring of 2012, I took part in the 5X50 Challenge. This popular challenge was aimed at encouraging those who signed up to make a self-propelled journey of at least five kilometres, every day for 50 consecutive days.

Taking part in the 5X50 Challenge prompted me to pause and analyse how I had been exercising prior to March 2012. I had certainly been active and could claim to be fairly fit, but what I had actually been doing, in a typical week, was going berserk for three days a week and being almost completely inactive for the other four. I would train with the running club on Thursday evenings and take part in various weekend activities, but my average Monday, Tuesday, Wednesday and Friday would be spent sitting at a desk and seldom raising my heart rate. The sudden change from days of inactivity to days of intense activity was also leading to injuries and a low base-level of fitness that I wasn't happy with. Once I realised what was happening I became determined to do something about it.

The potential health implications from those inactive days began to nag away at me and soon registered at the top of my *Do something about this* list. At that point I realised I needed a physical exercise challenge that would get me out taking exercise on a more regular basis than in the past, and 5X50 was, for me, the perfect way to create that sense of challenge.

I successfully completed the challenge, which ended in May, then made an effort to incorporate more exercise into the rest of that year, although looking back now I did that in a non-structured way. I didn't have a specific target, just a vague plan to take more exercise than I used to do before the 50 days of the challenge. That plan worked to some extent in that I did get out more often than before, but by the end of the year I knew that I needed a bit more focus to my exercise routine. I realised I was drifting backwards again. The 50 days of 5X50 had provided me with a form of discipline and focus that was missing after the challenge was over. As we approached the end of the year, and with thoughts turning towards new year's resolutions, my solution was to create my own challenge and re-install that sense of discipline and focus that I was looking for.

I really wanted to get back to enjoying the many benefits I had experienced during the 50 days of the challenge, so my answer was to set myself a long-term challenge. The lesson that the 5X50 Challenge had taught me was that having a challenge with some numbers attached to it was a great way of motivating myself, maintaining my focus and developing a strong determination to succeed. As for those many benefits that I just mentioned, they included improved sleep, higher base-level of fitness, a period of time set aside to wind down and de-stress, and

an opportunity to just enjoy being outdoors on a more regular basis.

So, at the beginning of 2013, I set out to make an active travel journey of at least five kilometres on 270 days in the year. The six activities that I would include in my challenge would be walking, running, cycling, canoeing, kayaking and skiing.

270 days, that was an easy enough target to achieve. After all, that would allow me up to 95 days in the year when I wouldn't have to go out. That would be slightly over five days per week of activity. I thought it was a realistic target at the start of the year. Anyway, I could always nudge it up to 300 during the year if I thought it was becoming too easy.

A concession to harsh winter conditions that I originally inserted into my challenge was that I would make a journey of at least five kilometres, or equivalent other exercise. This meant that a good session on a rowing machine or in the swimming pool, for example, would also count as my exercise for the day. So, as the new year began and my new exercise target kicked in, I managed to get out more than in the previous few months. By the end of January, I had completed 19 journeys of at least five kilometres, which, depending on how you look at it, was a decent start to the challenge or a pretty poor show given that there were 12 days when I hadn't managed to get out to exercise, although I had been on a rowing machine on one of those days.

I approached February with a bit more commitment and a determination to get back onto the required trajectory to achieve the 270 days target. Although I perhaps didn't appreciate it at the time, this kind of challenge can become mathematical. If I missed eight days per month (8 x 12 = 96), then I would end up on 269 days (365 − 96 = 269) at the end of the year. In other words, if I missed eight days per month up to November, but only seven days in December, then I would reach my 270 days target. However, going into February, I was already down on the target by four days. Time to get out more.

If this kind of challenge can become mathematical, it can also become meteorological and focused on daylight. I now have an increased awareness of how much more daylight there is in February compared to January, and how in February you can get out after 5.00 p.m. for a run or bike ride in the last of the daylight. I also found myself studying the weather forecast on the most ordinary of days in order to pick the optimum time for going out. If the day is going to start fine, but go downhill from 10.00 a.m. onwards then it makes sense to go out before work, but if a foul morning is going to be followed by an improving day and a dry, calm evening, then I would aim to get out at lunchtime or after work.

This heightened awareness of daylight and weather led to a much better performance in February. I managed to get out 25 times. I only missed three days, meaning that after two months I had missed a total of 15 days. I was back on target. I could go through the rest of the year missing eight days per month and I would end up on 270 days.

Ah, but what if we get some really bad weather in December? It would be wise to build up some credit, get ahead of the curve, just in case my challenge unravels in the last few days of the year. So, yet again, I entered a new month with even greater determination and a more tactical approach to the challenge, plus, it's pretty obvious to say, there was even more daylight to play with.

My statistics for March 2013 were 28 days when I got out to move my body at least five kilometres, and I went for a swim on one of the three days when I didn't get out. I was now well inside the line on the graph for reaching 270 days in the year. In fact, I was only just outside the line required to make it to 300 days. That was the point when I decided to ramp up the challenge and set myself a higher bar to clear.

As it turned out, the day that I went for the swim, 24 March 2013, was the last day that I didn't complete the five kilometres challenge that year. 25 March 2013 was the start of my unbroken streak of completing a journey of at least five kilometres every single day. So, by the end of 2013, I had a final score of 347 days on which I had made a self-propelled journey of at least five kilometres. From late March onwards, I had an overwhelming determination not to miss any day. I had made daily exercise a high priority and was building every day around taking some form of exercise. In some ways, this made the challenge much easier. Taking a day off was no longer an option. From that moment onwards, I have woken up each morning knowing that I will be making a self-propelled journey of at least five kilometres before the end of the day.

My challenge now is to make an active travel (self-propelled) journey of at least five kilometres every day. No more need for mathematics and a curve on a graph, just a determination to get out of the door. From 25 March 2013 onwards, the rule has been that the activity has to be on the day, every day. Trading activity, backwards or forwards, from one day to another is not allowed. A session on a rowing machine or other form of exercise would no longer count towards the challenge, although it would be a beneficial extra piece of exercise. As far as the challenge is concerned, it has to be me moving at least five kilometres.

The name given to an unbroken run of taking exercise every day is a *streak*. Running at least one mile every calendar day is known as a *runstreak*. What I'm doing is therefore an *exercise streak*. It's great being a streaker because you don't have to think about whether or not you are going out today. You just know that you *are* going out for some exercise, it's just a matter of when and how far, and in my case, which form of propulsion.

Since beginning my streak, I have passed various landmarks that have provided targets for me to aim for, achieve and move on from. At the beginning of 2014, I had my mind focused on one year, then it was 500 days, then a complete calendar year, two years, 1,000 days, a second complete calendar year, three years, a third complete calendar year. At the time of writing I have passed the eight-year mark and gone beyond 3,000 days.

A great deal of walking, running, cycling, paddling and skiing have taken place during that time, but what are the lessons that I can share from all that activity?

Well, first of all, it has given me a higher base-level of fitness. Not having the totally blank days means that I'm giving my body some kind of workout every day and therefore avoiding the one-step-forward, one-step-backwards scenario that I had before. I have built exercise into my daily routine. Having said that, I do recognise the very important requirement for the human body to rest and recover from its exertions, which is why my five kilometres of exercise on certain days is a very easy walk, maybe spread out over two or three outings. Somebody once said to me that "A five kilometre walk for you is nothing," to which I replied, "It can't be nothing, because it is something – every bit of movement counts".

I've had conversations with lots of people about this challenge over the last eight years and given a lot of thought to some of their comments and questions. One of the comments I hear is that you can't count a steady walk, or can't count skiing, or some other question about the rules that I have set myself. My answer is pretty simple, "My challenge, my rules". I made up the challenge, I tweaked it for a few months and then settled on a set of rules that challenge me and feel right to me.

Somebody else that I spoke to was clearly interested in doing something similar and asked if his walk home from college would count. I said it would count for me, but it would be up to you to make your own rules. You don't have to copy my rules to the letter. Like I keep saying, "You don't have to copy the person that inspires you. Use your imagination to channel inspiration into your own situation." Another interpretation of "My challenge, my rules" is: "Your challenge, your rules".

Benefits

When I completed my first year of the five kilometres challenge I was asked the simple question, "Why?".

It was so simple a question, and yet one that caused me to pause and think, and think some more. After two days I had an answer, albeit the person that had asked me the question was no longer on the other end of the phone. I've now had a few more years to think about this, so here are my thoughts on why I pursue this challenge.

Improved health is an obvious reason for taking regular exercise, and I am now much more aware of how my body is feeling. Exercise is a major contributor to improving and maintaining good health, but so is the right amount of rest. I therefore try to constantly think about what type of exercise my body needs on any given day. When I'm most in need of a rest I will take a walk on the basis that it will help keep my muscles moving and prevent my back from stiffening up, but won't place excessive stress on my system. Likewise, a five kilometres bike ride with no hill to climb and without a sprint section is, for me, a very gentle workout.

A high level of fitness is also important to me, and I do see improved fitness as an important benefit of taking regular exercise. My challenge provides a higher base-level of fitness than I had before 2013, and that enables me to reach an even higher level and then a peak when, for example, I have a race that I want to do well in. While I don't run as fast as I did 30 years ago, I do still run in races at distances ranging from 800 metres up to full marathons, so there are times when I train to build stamina for long distance runs and other times when I train more for speed. When I'm running in a marathon in the middle of summer, I appreciate the fact that easy walks and bike rides the previous winter played their part in building my fitness and keeping me injury free in the build-up to that race.

While I have suffered a few injuries during the time I've been keeping to this five kilometres challenge, my overall feeling is that the regular exercise has reduced the number and seriousness of the injuries that I have had. The increased level of fitness has resulted in being more resilient to injuries and less likely to become injured because I'm never going out to do something big after three days of inactivity. A recurring problem that I do suffer from, however, is a disc issue in my lower back. This can still flare up and cause me pain if I don't manage it properly, but it now happens less frequently, and when it does I get out for a steady walk to keep it moving, rather than staying indoors and avoiding movement.

I do have to admit that I have often struggled to get sufficient sleep. That's not to say I have been a raging insomniac, but over the years there have been too many nights when I have not managed to get sufficient sleep and I have struggled through the following day. Now, I haven't carried out any scientific study into my sleep patterns, so any comment I make here is purely anecdotal, but my feeling is that my problem nights in the past followed days when I hadn't exercised, and while I can still have the occasional problem night, I am far better at sleeping now than I was in the past.

Another reason I keep grinding out the journeys and mounting up the days is down to my competitive spirit. I am just driven to take on challenges like this and to maintain my focus. The original challenge of 270 days in the year soon turned out to be too easy for me, so I raised the bar to 300 and then to 365. I could just set the target at 350 or 360, and accept that there may just be a handful of days in the year when I can't get out for a quick run or bike ride, but that isn't in my chemistry. The target is now set at 365 or 366 days in the year, and one way or the other, I do get out there and cover the distance.

Which neatly leads onto my final reason for setting myself this challenge – I just enjoy doing it. That's why I keep doing it. I derive great pleasure from exercise, and I want some of it every single day.

As with a lot of things in life, my approach is to set up a spreadsheet, so this challenge is monitored by a spreadsheet to record the type of exercise I take each day and keep track of the number of days since the challenge began. I've tweaked the spreadsheet a little over the years, partly to record more information and to record additional data for some of the sub-challenges that I've added to the main challenge (more on that later).

As for the future of this challenge, well, I can't keep it going forever. When I do finally miss a day, I may choose to amend the challenge or set myself a different target and re-set the counter to zero. In the meantime, the five kilometres per day target is providing me with a great deal of fun as well as a reasonably demanding challenge and the range of benefits discussed above. However, in researching this book I've discovered what other people are doing and there are lessons there in terms of the other ways of taking daily exercise. Whatever comes next, I know that I will want to continue finding time for regular exercise and pushing myself to pursue a challenge that I enjoy and delivers the same range of benefits.

Making regular exercise a habit

I had a long discussion with a friend while I was writing this chapter and he came out with an interesting observation that I hadn't thought about before. He said, "Daily exercise is no longer a challenge for you, it's become a habit. Motivation is what gets you started; habit is what keeps you going. You don't need motivation to get out there every day, because you are so into the habit of just doing it." He has a point, but I would say that getting out every day is still a challenge and does require a level of motivation, but the habit of doing it does make it far easier.

Research into habit formation has shown that engaging in a behaviour over a period of time can help ingrain that behaviour so that it eventually becomes habitual. Some say that the critical length of time for this to occur is as short as 30 days.

Another important aspect of finding time for exercise every day is that I plan ahead and build it into my day without having to cancel or curtail other commitments. There is a criticism often levelled at people who are seen as being addicted to exercise, that they will forego social activities because they have to go for a run instead of meeting with friends or visiting relatives. I think it is important to be aware of that danger, but believe it is possible to keep taking regular exercise, consider what is in the best interests of my health, and maintain a balanced social life. If I arrange to meet up with friends I just might, for example, choose to take a longer walk to and from our meeting place. I just see that as recognising the need for, and benefits of, regular exercise, and looking out for opportunities within my day to include plenty of movement.

I certainly recognise that it is possible to go over the top and exercise too much, but when words like addiction and obsession are used, sometimes fairly but often unfairly, I tend to respond with the line that when something that appears to one person to be an obsession or addiction, to someone else represents dedication or commitment. I always aim to maintain a sense of fun, humour and enjoyment in my exercise activities and believe that is what keeps me in the dedicated and committed zone.

Bread-and-butter

Like most other active people, I live for the highest quality days, walking along mountain ridges in perfect weather or cycling eighty or ninety miles with the sea on one side and mountains on the other. But, in order to keep this challenge ticking over I need to keep going out on days when the weather is far from brilliant, and the easiest and quickest option is to just go out from home for a quick five kilometre bike ride. I call these the bread-and-butter days. In culinary terms, I prefer vegetable burrito or veggie-haggis lasagne days, but there are days when it's just more realistic to have the exercise equivalent of bread-and-butter. There are days when I don't even get changed into full cycling gear, I just pop on some cycling leggings and shoes and whiz round my local five-kilometre loop. In the winter months in particular, I tend to go for a quick ride on the bike at lunchtime, then get back in time for lunch and an afternoon at work.

One way that I look at this is that the bread-and-butter days keep me fit for when those exceptional days come along, but another way of viewing them is that they sometimes turn up the most amazing experiences on what looked like being a bog-standard outing. There are days when I am rewarded for just being out there by a sighting of a red squirrel or suddenly finding myself running behind a sparrowhawk in flight, or I bump into someone cycling from Ardnamurchan to Lowestoft and pause for a chat.

I also enjoy playing games by varying the route slightly from day-to-day, or saying I'm only going out to cycle five kilometres, but once I'm out there I extend my route to a ten or fifteen kilometre circuit. I wouldn't have contemplated going so far when I looked out of the window, but once I'm actually out there, I quite often get the urge to add on a bit of extra distance. Also, there's a particular stretch of my local loop that is flat, straight and almost free from traffic, so I quite often wind-up for a real sprint along that section. I do this to get the legs and heart pumping, as well as just getting the buzz from the thrill of the speed.

A blast of outdoor exercise on a lunchtime is also a great way to clear your head and let the sub-conscious mind take over. I quite regularly get halfway round the circuit and have an idea for something that I'm working on, so there's many a day when I get back and instantly write down a thought that I had while out on my bike or running along the trail.

Although I have a regular loop, with several possible variations, I take the approach that I should seek every opportunity to exercise somewhere else. If I'm going to be away from home at any time in the day, be it for work, shopping, visiting friends or whatever, then I make every effort to use that time away to fit in a run, walk or bike ride. It isn't always possible, but when it is, it is a day when I get to exercise somewhere different and I avoid the well-worn trip around the usual route. It also gives me the opportunity on certain days to take exercise with someone else, which gives the added bonus of sharing the journey and having a chat.

At this point, I feel that I need to emphasise the *at least* aspect in my challenge. Even on the bread-and-butter days, my challenge is to travel *at least five kilometres*. There are many days, indeed the majority of days, when I go further than that. I quite often set out with the intention of walking or cycling five kilometres, but get back having gone some way beyond that target.

Quirky and amusing

Over the course of several years, there have been a few journeys that have had, let's say, a quirky element to them, and could be seen as amusing or perhaps even embarrassing. Here's a brief sample of some of those more unusual journeys.

Having checked-in our bags for a flight at Turin Airport, there was going to be a wait of nearly three hours before take-off. The option for how to spend the first of those hours was to go through security and mooch around the shops or go for a five kilometre walk. It was an easy choice to make. The sun was shining outside the airport, but it would be dark and almost certainly cold and raining by the time we got home, so the walk was the obvious option. Airports aren't the most interesting places in the world to walk from. Nevertheless, we did manage to complete a five-kilometre walk which mainly consisted of several laps of the coach and car parks. Nobody asked us what we were doing, but we did feel conspicuous and wouldn't have been surprised if we had been asked to explain our suspicious actions.

A lorry fire on a French autoroute closed the road for over two hours and we were held up in the resultant traffic jam. Unable to fully converse in the various debates as to when we might get moving again, we decided to walk up and down the hard shoulder while recording the distance travelled and never venturing more than 600 metres from our car. As well as fitting our daily exercise into an unforeseen slot in the day, we managed to remain calm when others were getting stressed about being late for their next appointment, and when we did eventually reach our accommodation we had at least completed our five-kilometre walk.

My partner is also taking on the same five-kilometre per day exercise challenge, which means that we have the pleasure and motivation that comes from sharing the challenge and the benefits, as well as the humour when things turn a bit quirky. In the summer of 2017, Fiona's work involved a 10-day trip on a research ship in the North Sea. The back deck of the ship was the only place to go for a run or walk, but its maximum width was a mere eight metres. So, after doing the division on her calculator, and armed with a click counter, she set out to complete at least 625 widths of the ship in a series of shuttle runs – much to the bemusement of the boat crew.

Five-course meals

While there have been many bread-and-butter days, and a few quirky days, there have also been plenty of unforgettable days that were five-course meals in comparison to the helpings of bread-and-butter. Since starting this exercise streak I have:

- Cycled from Land's End to John O'Groats in 2013, taking 14 days to cover 1,746 kilometres.
- Cycled from Mizen to Malin, the Irish end-to-end, in 2014.
- Run five marathons, namely the Brixen (uphill) Marathon in Italy in 2015 and 2018, the Cape Wrath Marathon in 2016, Glencoe Marathon in 2017 and Jungfrau Marathon in Switzerland in 2019.
- Competed in the first four Vertical Kilometre (VK) races to be held in Scotland between 2016 and 2019.
- Had over 100 days walking and running in the Scottish mountains.

- Kayaked some of Scotland's spectacular coastline.

I need my bread-and-butter days for all the benefits that I've mentioned previously, but I treasure my five-course meal days because those are the ones that I live for, they are the days that stay in the memory and fill me with absolute joy.

PRINCIPLE NUMBER 3

My challenge, my rules -
Your challenge, your rules.

PRINCIPLE NUMBER 4

Get out on the bread-and-butter days, and relish the five-course meal days.

9

The annual cycle

When you take regular exercise in the outdoors, you gain a heightened sense of the changing seasons, and lengthening and shortening of the daylight hours. Given the importance of daylight for outdoor exercise, another aspect of the way I challenge myself to make a journey of at least five kilometres every day is that I have a different strategy for the different seasons of the year.

You won't be surprised to hear me say that winter is the hardest season to stay motivated and keep getting out day after day. However, it's not the lashing rain that provides the biggest challenge. By watching the forecasts, that can usually be avoided. You would be surprised how few times I go out in the rain – even in Scotland. That said, I am in the east of Scotland. Readers in the west of Scotland have their own weather systems!

No, the main issues are darkness and frost. About once a week I run under streetlights or on a floodlit track with a running club, but for the rest of the week I live way beyond the reach of streetlights, so if I don't get out before nightfall it tends to be a case of running or walking with a headtorch on, or cycling with good front and rear lights. As a result, I do try to get out as often as possible on lunchtimes or straight after breakfast, usually on the bike, but sometimes to run or walk. Being out in daylight in mid-winter is so important. We are only just beginning to understand the psychological and physical benefits of daylight during the darkest part of the year and regular exercise on a lunchtime is a great way of gaining those benefits. Nevertheless, I really enjoy getting my headtorch on and going out for a walk or run after dark in winter. Just not every night of the week.

Frost and ice are also a big consideration in winter and can have a major impact on the exercise options that are available. I was out on my bike one lunchtime in December 2014 when I hit a patch of ice and ended up on the tarmac with a badly bruised hip. I've been much more cautious about cycling on frosty days since then and will quite often opt for a run or walk now instead of risking a similar accident. Again, this is now built into my weather-watching activities and forms a part of my decisions on when to go out and which activity to choose on a particular day.

After picking my way through a winter, getting out on lunchtimes and avoiding cycling in icy conditions, it's always a relief to reach the springtime and suddenly feel the freshness and warmth, hear the sound of birds singing again and revel in the daylight that comes with lengthening days. There comes that point in the year where you're beginning to think that you will never see any decent daylight again, then spring arrives, the days draw out once more and all of a sudden there is usable light after work. In fact, there is so much daylight in the month of March, that I have now started living on British Summer Time from the end of February onwards. The options for taking exercise early in the evening, in daylight, suddenly open up. I start to get that feeling of having made it through the winter and the challenge of getting out at some point on every day is so much easier again.

Depending on your routine and commitments to other people, you might want to try this. Through the deep winter months, I usually get out of bed when it's still dark, but by the end of February I get up and it's already daylight. I realised I was lying in bed on a morning while it was light outside, then bemoaning the fact that it was getting dark around 6.00 p.m. So, what I do now is move onto British Summer Time (daylight saving) one month before the rest of the country, at the end of February, rather than end of March. I just move my whole day forward an hour to give me an extra hour of daylight on a morning, plus an extra hour of usable daylight after my working day. It's brilliant. I wish I had thought about it sooner.

This system wouldn't be so easy for anyone working in a rigid nine-to-five type job (imagine a teacher asking his or her pupils to come in an hour early for the month of March!), but even in that situation, it would be possible to switch some tasks from the evening to the morning. It just takes a bit of imagination and some determination.

When the rest of the nation move their clocks forward in late March, I'm already there waiting for them, and at that point we all have light until 8.00 p.m. and there will be light evenings for the next six months. The challenge of taking exercise every single day suddenly becomes a whole lot easier. If I managed to keep getting out every day through the six dark months (October to March) then the six light months (April to September) will be far easier. Yes, there will be days when it is logistically hard to fit in a quick run or bike ride but, on the whole, the availability of daylight makes it so much easier to get out early on a morning or late in the evening, and without there being the danger of icy roads or paths.

Compared to the dark winter months, exercising in summer is relatively easy. Light evenings open up a whole range of opportunities. After five months of coming out of work to be greeted by darkness and then running under streetlights or with a headtorch, there is suddenly the joy of evening bike rides, evening hill walks and, for competitive runners, of evening road and hill races. When the weather or daily schedule pushes me in that direction I will still cycle five kilometres before breakfast or run at lunchtime, but the opening up of light evenings means that on the majority of days I can get out after work for a quick spin on the bike, run up a hill or take the kayak out onto the estuary. The options are almost limitless.

As the months go by and we eventually drift into October and towards the clocks moving back once more, the process goes into reverse and the light evenings get taken away from us again. Day-by-day the emphasis shifts back towards getting out at lunchtime on a more regular basis and building up a determination to keep the challenge going through the winter months ahead. A crucial part of preparing for the coming winter is to think about batteries. In September or October each year, I always check the batteries in my headtorch, as well as my bike lights and bike helmet lights, replacing any that show signs of fading. I also make sure there is a good set of spare headtorch batteries in my rucksack lid. A bit of forward planning and a renewed determination to keep the challenge going through the winter always helps me get ready for the onset of another Scottish winter and a fresh round of cold, dark, bread-and-butter days.

You will have gathered by now that, in a moth-like way, I am drawn to daylight. I just want to be outdoors whenever there is natural daylight in the sky. When I was young I only enjoyed going to the cinema if it was dark outside, and even now, I regard the cinema as somewhere to go in winter. The thought of sitting in a darkened cinema when it's light outside is just beyond contemplation. Why would you want to do that? I accept that Hollywood, Bollywood, Pinewood Studios and the rest of the movie industry couldn't survive if everyone had a 6-month cinema-going season, but for me, sitting in a cinema in summer is just a waste of valuable, usable daylight. I might make the occasional exception for horrendous weather or a very good film, but only on very rare occasions. That said, I do enjoy a relaxing evening out at the cinema in winter, but in summer I would just rather be walking in the outdoors or in the garden enjoying good conversation and birdsong.

Another aspect of my annual cycle that I find to be vital in keeping me going through the winter is the value of reviewing the year about to end and planning for the year ahead. My preference is to review the old year around mid-December and write down my plans for the following year in the days between Christmas and new year.

Another review that sports fans in Britain get involved in around mid-December is the annual BBC Sports Personality of the Year (SPOTY) awards. I've been watching this programme and voting since (now let me work this one out) around about 1967. Back in those days I had to send in a postcard to register my vote, whereas nowadays it's a simple click on the phone during the programme. I love SPOTY and enjoy that look back at the sporting year, but in this social media age, and thinking about the need for the nation to become more active, I think there's another review we should all be doing at that time of year – reviewing our own sporting (or activity) year.

That's why I started a hashtag in December 2016, #MSH2016. MSH stands for My Sporting Highlight and the idea is you attach one photograph that sums up your own personal sporting/activity highlight of the year, along with a brief description. This has to be your own activity, not something you watched someone else doing. Watching your team win the cup doesn't count. It has to be something that you were physically involved with.

So, as well as celebrating the successes of our national sporting heroes and re-living the Olympics, World Cups, Wimbledon, test matches, Ryder Cup, Formula One World Championship and so on, let's also take some time to think about what we achieved in the year. It might be far less spectacular, but it should bring back a happy memory, remind us of an achievement to be proud of and contain a story that we can share on social media. Completing your first parkrun or crossing the finish line alongside your six-year-old daughter are the kinds of highlights that I have in mind. They're not going to win awards on SPOTY, but they're fantastic memories to re-live and fun to share. Most importantly, they have the effect of inspiring other people.

We all tend to make improvements in our lives when something happens to inspire us, and while the achievements of Team GB Olympians on our television screens can inspire us to become more active, so too can the more down-to-earth achievements of our friends, relatives, work colleagues and contacts on social media. The point I'm making is that we need to recognise and celebrate achievement at all levels, because achievement inspires, whatever the level of achievement.

PRINCIPLE NUMBER 5

Have a winter strategy so that you maintain the motivation through the cold, dark, wet months.

10

Sub-challenges and targets for the year

Given that my overall challenge for any given year is to make an active travel journey of at least five kilometres every day, I now have a bit of fun each year by setting myself a series of smaller sub-challenges to aim for throughout the year. If the daily five-kilometre journey is the bread-and-butter, the sub-challenges provide the spicy sandwich filling to liven things up a bit. So, picking on a recent year to look at, before the start of 2017 I set myself the following list of six challenges for the year:

1. Cycle 2,017 miles
2. Run a marathon
3. Run 17 parkruns
4. Run 4 new parkruns
5. Run a sub-3-minute 800 metres
6. Run the Marcothon

At the end of the year I had succeeded in all six of those

challenges. I cycled a total distance of 2,066 miles in the year (target was 2,017), ran the Glencoe Marathon in October (target was one Marathon), ran 24 parkruns (target was 17) of which 8 were new ones (target was 4), ran 800 metres in 2 minutes 50.01 seconds (target was 3 minutes) and the final sub-challenge for the year, in that it couldn't start until 1 December and could only be successfully completed on 31 December, was the Marcothon. The Marcothon, which is explained in Appendix 1: *Other Popular Challenges*, involves running at least five kilometres every day through the entire month of December.

The sub-challenges certainly added a bit of extra motivation in 2017, and that cycling target of 2,017 miles pushed me to make some longer rides throughout the year. There were lots of days when I went out to ride seven or eight miles but came back having ridden 15 or 20. I eventually completed mile 2,017 on 18 November. My plan was to complete that sub-challenge before the end of November, in order to clear the decks for concentrating on running in December and having a shot at the Marcothon. My strategy worked, and I was able to run the Marcothon without having the cycle challenge overlapping into December.

That was a detailed look at my sub-challenges for 2017. In December 2017, I sat down and came up with a different set of sub-challenges for 2018.

This chapter has looked at targets for the year, but let's just end on the shorter-term targets for each week and even each day. As well as making an active journey of at least five kilometres every day, I also take time out to stretch several times throughout the day, and over the course of a week I aim to get out of breath at least twice. The benefits of stretching are explained in Chapter 25: *Sleep, hydration, exercise, diet and stretching (SHEDS)*.

There's no scientific basis for my getting out of breath target and it is just a vague aim rather than strict challenge, but it does mean that I try to find time for exercise sessions that will push me harder than some of the softer days where I'm just walking or going for a steady bike ride.

The benefits of getting out of breath include an increase in the strength and functioning of muscles, making them more efficient. Muscles then require less oxygen to move and they produce less carbon dioxide. This subsequently reduces the amount of air needed to breathe in and out for any given exercise. Exercises that involve getting out of breath are also likely to improve the body's circulation and strengthen the heart. So, while exercises that get you out of breath can feel like hard work and create a feeling of pain, the result can be an overall improvement in your body's efficiency. That's where the "No pain – No gain" saying comes from.

Taking sub-challenges to a really micro-level, I sometimes like to set spontaneous wee challenges for myself, like saying, "walk as fast as you can to the next lamppost". I just let my imagination loose to come up with these quick challenges, because they add an element of fun and have the effect of raising my heart rate, thereby increasing the benefits from the exercise I'm taking at the time.

I have included this short chapter on my personal goals for the year ahead to encourage you to think about what your short- and medium-term goals might be. Do you want to set a series of goals for the next 12 months as well as having an ongoing exercise challenge? I will return to this in Chapter 26: *But, what about me? I hear you ask.*

That's the story of my challenge, but before going on to look at what your challenge might be, let's take a look at what a range of other people are doing.

PART 3

Other People and
Their Challenges

11

Five reasons why

As I go deeper and deeper into my own challenge, I find myself becoming increasingly interested in other people's challenges. The rich spectrum of what others are doing absolutely fascinates me. I just can't get enough of hearing the wide range of ways in which people are challenging themselves and finding methods and routines to build exercise into their lives.

This has resulted in developing a real interest and enthusiasm to find out what other activities people are taking on in order to challenge themselves, and what motivates them to start and then continue. Whether it is the radical challenges of running every day for over 50 years, or the other end of the spectrum where people are setting what might appear to be simple targets, but which for them can represent a major effort and significant change to their routines. So, while I love hearing about the extreme end of that spectrum, I am equally passionate about the person that decides to climb the stairs to the 7th floor instead of taking the lift, or builds a 15-minute lunchtime walk into their busy daily schedule, or sets out to cycle 1,000 miles in the year at the age of 87.

There are a number of 'off-the-shelf' challenges that attract mass participation, and Part 4 will look at a selection of those, but for many people a challenge is a personal invention that they develop for themselves. These personal challenges can have their roots in one of the mass-participation challenges, or they can just be the result of an imaginative mind. Wherever these challenges come from, I really appreciate hearing about them and adding them to my list of fun ways to set an exercise target.

The next few pages are devoted to the stories of ten individuals who told me about their personal challenges. In each case I asked the same six questions.

1. What's your challenge?
2. How long have you been doing it?
3. What motivated you to start?
4. What motivates you to continue?
5. What difference has it made to your life?
6. What's your message to anyone that isn't taking regular exercise?

The comments and background stories I recorded from these interviews are presented here under the following headings that capture the main reasons for choosing to increase your levels of physical activity:

- Concerns about being overweight
- Issues relating to mental health
- Concerns about physical health
- A desire to be proactive and prevent health-related problems

- A desire to improve your strength and fitness levels.

While it is clearly possible to see exercise as contributing to two or more of these reasons at the same time, I have attempted to categorise each interviewee under the heading that appeared most relevant to the individual; however several of them stated that they probably fitted into more than one of the categories.

I mentioned earlier about reactive and proactive reasons for becoming more physically active and looking at the five reasons in the list above, the first three are reactive reasons, whereas the last two are more proactive. I was tempted to have another proactive category of becoming more active for fun and enjoyment, but decided that whatever your reason for taking physical exercise, it has to be fun and you need to enjoy it, so fun and enjoyment are overarching rather than being a separate category.

As you read through the ten stories in the next five chapters, I hope you will pick up the sense of fun and enjoyment that those people are gaining from their activities. The distances that Stuart and Daile are running might not sound like fun to some readers, and I know you can only read their words as opposed to hear their voices, but hopefully you will gain a sense of their passion and how much they are enjoying what they are doing.

I also hope there will be a line, somewhere in one of the interviews in Chapters 12 to 17 or one of the examples in Chapter 18: *Other inspirational stories*, that will make you go, "That's it, that's got a connection to my situation, that's what I need to do".

12

Weight

As someone who has never had a weight problem, I recognise how lucky I have been in that respect and appreciate how some people struggle more than others to control their weight.

While some people take little or no exercise and, perhaps not surprisingly, put on weight, others take a fair amount of exercise and have a reasonable diet, but still struggle to maintain a healthy weight. Nevertheless, short of invasive surgery, exercise and diet are the two main ways of controlling the weight of our bodies.

This chapter looks at two individuals who have recognised they have weight problems and turned to exercise in their efforts to get on top of their issues.

I've known **Zoe** for at least 15 years, and she has always been open in terms of discussing her weight, so when I decided to dedicate a chapter to this issue she was an obvious choice for someone to interview.

Sean was introduced to me at the end of a recent parkrun and to begin with he didn't appear to be a candidate for a place in the chapter on concerns about being overweight; at least not until he told me that he had been to within a pound of 17 stones, at which point he decided to act. His work as a teacher helped him recognise the problems he was having and played a significant part in his route back to better health and fitness.

Here are their stories in their own words.

Zoe

What is your challenge?
My challenge is to find a way of getting fit enough to achieve four targets, one in running, two in terms of lifting weights and one to do five press-ups, plus I want to achieve a lifestyle that works with my life as a kayak coach.

The challenges that that throws up to me are about time away from home, so in the summer I'm away a lot. My job is active, but relative to my own fitness level I can't really count it as exercise. So, what I feel I need to do is schedule my exercise around my work in order that I improve my own fitness and find a way of working my lifestyle to mean that I'm happy with the way that I feel and the way that I look.

So, workwise I'm kayak coaching and hillwalking. In terms of my own exercise, kayaking can be exercise, but just not normally with clients, so mostly running, cycling and strength and conditioning training.

"My job is active, but relative to my own fitness level I can't really count it as exercise."

How long have you been doing it?
The first thing to say is I've been doing it my whole life. So, all my life I've struggled with my weight and my fitness. I

was the person at school that was least likely to do anything related to sport, so the fact that I'm actually doing sport for a living now is as much of a surprise to me as it is to everyone else.

But, in terms of this time around, a year and a half with a certain level of commitment, but really really committed to it for the last three months.

"I was the person at school that was least likely to do anything related to sport."

What motivated you to start?

Again, for me it's always about my weight and fitness level, and how that makes me feel about myself. I've been working with a personal trainer since I started a year and a half ago, so the motivation at that point was that I'd just got fed up with the way that I felt about myself, the impact it had on my confidence, always feeling and looking overweight, so I felt I needed to change something. I was really struggling with getting to the end of a summer season, working away a lot during that season, eating out in the evening with clients and eating hotel food, which, let's face it, is not healthy. Not when you're doing it day in day out. Yet, I felt I was being expected to look a particular way and to have a particular level of fitness, because I am paid to be fit as a kayaking coach. The thing that gave me a real kick up the arse this time around, the trainer that I've been working with posted something on Facebook. It was a really simple thing, it was a picture of a banana and it just said, "If you're not hungry enough to eat a piece of fruit, you're not hungry, you're bored". I just thought, you know what, you're absolutely right. I've struggled my whole life with overeating and not being able to properly control my own appetite. I've just not had a very healthy relationship with food. I think I've never really understood what it feels like to be full. I think my body doesn't do a very good job of telling me when that happens, or it certainly didn't. So, I just kind of looked at that phrase and went, "Blimey, I think I know what I need to do". I had a lightbulb moment.

"I'd just got fed up with the way that I felt about myself, the impact it had on my confidence, always feeling and looking overweight."

What motivates you to continue?

Progress. Because it's working. Three-and-a-bit months in I have to say that I've worked really hard and I guess the other thing is that it's part of my job really. I'm paid to be fit, so it is part of my job to look the way that people expect me to look to a certain extent and to have the level of fitness that people are paying me to have. So, that's part of my motivation, but essentially what I've done is limit my calorie intake, but not ridiculously. I've limited myself to 1,800 calories regardless of the exercise I do, give or take. There's the odd day where I feel hungry and need a bit more. Working with my personal trainer doing strength training and I think the important thing for me was we set some really specific goals, so they were SMART goals. They were absolutely Specific, Measurable, Achievable, Realistic and Timebound, and there were four of them. So, it wasn't just one thing to focus on. The key for me was it wasn't focused on losing weight, so they were fitness-based goals, but in order to achieve them I would have to get lighter. Particularly the running one. So, I was going to have to get lighter in order to achieve that and it was something that I really wanted to do. It's been years and years that I just haven't been able to do it, and that goal is to run five kilometres in 30 minutes, which I've now done, this morning.

So, there was the five kilometres in 30 minutes, deadlift 89.5 kilograms, because that was all the weights that I owned at the time, I've since bought more weights because I achieved that target. Then the two that I haven't done yet, I want to back squat 70 kilograms and the reason for that weight is that's how much my partner weighs, and the other one is I've never been able to do a press-up, so I want to do five press-ups. So, that was the initial goal-setting exercise, which has got me to the first three months and the timescale for those was the end of April, so I've still got three weeks to go. The important thing about all that is that I set those goals. It was my timescale, my targets, my rules, my everything. My challenge, my rules.

I also knew quite a bit about running training and how to get faster, I just never managed to get fast enough before. My personal trainer built intervals into my strength and conditioning sessions, but anything other than that in terms of running, I did myself. I had control over what I was doing, although I obviously have him programming my strength and conditioning sessions, because I don't know enough to do that myself. He knows exactly when to push me and when not, and that's all done online.

So, what motivates me to continue is just progress, it's working, I've lost ten kilograms, I've got faster, taken five minutes off my 5k time. I think I'm the strongest I've ever been and I'm feeling it in my everyday life, and in my boat I feel I can move better and I'm stronger on the water. I'm very conscious that I turn 43 this week, I'm getting older and I do a physical job, so if I'm going to carry on doing this job I'm going to have to find ways of preventing injuries. There's a whole lifestyle wrapped up in this one challenge, just longevity as well as my own confidence and my own psychological well-being, as well as my physical well-being.

"The important thing about all that is that I set those goals. It was my timescale, my targets, my rules, my everything. My challenge, my rules."

What difference has it made to your life?

It's made a massive difference.

I put this in a blog post last week. I saw a photo of myself, running at Alness last weekend, and it was the first time in my 43 years that I've seen a photo of me doing physical activity, other than kayaking, and I have not wanted to delete it. I've not had a sense of, "I hate that photo, don't show it to me". It's just a photo snapped by a marshal, on their phone, but it's the first time I've ever looked at a photo of me like that and not been slightly disgusted by it. I genuinely look in the mirror and don't recognise myself. I expect to see something that I don't see now, and I just feel better. I just feel better.

So, what difference has it made? I actually find it hard to put into words. It's just changed everything.

"I just feel better."

What's your message to anyone that isn't taking regular exercise?

Do it. Change something. I suppose my main message is, you don't have to get up and run a marathon. You just have to do something that feels challenging to you. You'll feel better about yourself in every possible way. It will be hard. I'm not saying it's going to be easy.

The things I share on Facebook and my blog posts, that's the nice stuff, that's not the tears at 9.00 at night when I feel rubbish and still have to do my gym session, because I've just driven 300 miles and got home just wanting to go to bed and have to get up again at 5.00 the next morning.

So, it won't be easy, but that's actually what makes it more rewarding. You know you've shed blood and sweated tears over it and that's what makes it so powerful. Everybody is going to be different, but just get up and do it because it's going to be worth it.

"You just have to do something that feels challenging to you."

Sean

What is your challenge?

My challenge is to lose weight and improve my fitness and overall health after a period of significant weight loss. My latest challenge on that journey has been to take part in parkrun, which a friend had been persistently asking me to get involved with. I'd kept putting it off, but when I eventually went I thought, "I can actually do this, this isn't too difficult for me".

How long have you been doing it?

Parkrun, I've only been involved for about six weeks, but I

have been working on my running for about a year, mainly through my work doing the Daily Mile. So, I've been building it up and doing some runs on my own and with my wife who has been doing the Couch to 5K Challenge[26]. So, she's been doing that and sticking to the programme and I've been running with her and then made the decision to go to parkrun. I started that six weeks ago and it's been going well. Every week I've done it I've improved my time, and I have been able to see a big change in that I'm running more and walking less each week.

"I have been able to see a big change in that I'm running more and walking less each week."

What motivated you to start?
I'd put on a lot of weight over a long period of time. There was a two-year period when I went from about 14 stones up to nearly 17 and I was still creeping upwards. I was very conscious of the fact that I'd put on a lot of weight, so I decided to combat that by going to Slimming World and that was very successful in that I lost three stones very quickly. Because I'd lost weight I felt that my physical fitness had improved just by dieting. I was less breathless, I was able to move around a lot more easily, so I was going out with the kids that I work with at the school and were doing the Daily Mile. When I was overweight I wasn't able to do the Daily Mile with them. I'd try to run it with them, but I'd soon be out of breath, so I'd have to pull out or just not run it at all and disappoint the pupils. When I lost the weight, I was motivated to take part in the Daily Mile with the kids. I would start off with a fast walk or jog for the first lap and then build it up. Then

the pupils were encouraging me to take part and to chase them and play games with them, and because of that I found myself increasing how much I was doing with them, without realising I was doing it. I could feel myself improving, so that kept me motivated and pushed me, to the point where I was running the whole three laps in a decent time around 10 to 15 minutes.

Then a friend who had been constantly encouraging me to come along to this thing called parkrun, which I'd never heard of before, and I was quite insistent that I'm not ready for that kind of distance or level of fitness. Anyway, she said come along and try it, and I kept putting it off and putting it off, but I was getting to that point where my weight had plateaued, so I thought I need to push myself and challenge myself now to do something different. Try to knock off a few more pounds and work on my fitness, so I went along to parkrun and did my first one in 34 minutes and from what I was told by a few folk, that was actually quite a good time for a first-timer. Considering I ran half of it, and walked-ran the other half, like ran a minute, walked a minute, I was quite impressed with the fact I was able to do that. That really motivated me to keep going, so I was back the next week and I was really keen. I was out to beat that 34 minutes, which I did, I got it down to 33. I then had a week off on holiday and came back the next week thinking I would have lost my momentum but surprised myself by going even faster. I really want to keep going with it, whereas by now I would normally have given up.

"Try to knock off a few more pounds and work on my fitness, so I went along to parkrun …"

What motivates you to continue?

I want to maintain the fitness and weight loss. There's also the vanity side, more looking at it from an aesthetic point of view, to shape up. I do still have a bit of gut that has not disappeared so by running I'm noticing that my body shape is changing, which is really good. Another reason is my family history. There's lots of heart problems in my family, diabetes and so on. Some of it has been caused by smoking, but there is a hereditary issue as well, which was undiagnosed for a long time until my mum had surgery and the biggest part was this hereditary condition that was from her father's side of the family. That motivated me to be thinking on a grander scale. It's not just about my weight and aesthetics, it's also about longevity and cardiovascular health as well, because I've got this history. I'm not a drinker or smoker, but I've suffered from high blood pressure, stress and anxiety, which isn't great for your heart. I thought, this is going to have to be combatted, so that's another reason for being motivated to keep going and reap the long-term benefits.

> *"It's not just about my weight and aesthetics, it's also about longevity and cardiovascular health as well."*

What difference has it made to your life?

I'm now down to bang on 14 stones, but my target weight is to get down to 13 stones 10 pounds, so I'm still trying to get it down a bit more.

It's still early days, but I do notice quite a big difference in my overall fitness. I'm sleeping better at night. Since I've increased my exercise levels I've got into a better sleep routine, I'm going to bed at a consistent time and waking up with more energy. Also, I've just been able to move around at a better pace and my confidence has been boosted. One of the good things for me is that I've suffered in the past from depression and anxiety, and I was on medication for about two years, but since I've been running I've not had to take my tablets. While I've been running I've found that it relieves stress, it helps calm me down, which has been really beneficial. Given that I'm a teacher and I've got quite a stressful job, if I maintain this when I go back to work after the summer holidays, I'd like to see how this benefits me in the workplace, because I think it's going to have a positive effect. It should give me more energy, help build my stamina in the classroom, particularly as I'm going to be working with an older class next year and teaching more demanding PE lessons with more physical involvement, as well as leading the Daily Mile.

Like I say, just appearance wise, it's really helped me, I do see my body shape changing, which is really good, but it's also made life that much better and I'm happier and healthier and I feel the benefits and I've now got into parkrun as well as the Daily Mile. I have seen that change build and that's really motivated me.

"Since I've increased my exercise levels I've got into a better sleep routine, I'm going to bed at a consistent time and waking up with more energy."

What's your message to anyone that isn't taking regular exercise?
Don't say "No". I kept putting it off. People kept saying to me, "You should try this – You should do this – You should take

part in parkrun – You should go for a run or join a group". Even when I was taking the Daily Mile at school, the pupils would say, "Do it with us," but I kept saying, "No, I'll just stand here at the side and watch you guys running round doing your Daily Mile," so I was always avoiding exercise, always avoiding admitting I was overweight.

So, my advice would be, just don't say "No". If, in your heart of hearts, you know that you need to do something, if you need to exercise, if you're needing to make those life changes, whether it be for weight loss, fitness, strength, whatever, then don't say "No," just say "Yes" and try it. The first couple of times can be hard but keep pushing yourself. It's the same with the parkrun, every week I go I'm motivated and I'm asking, "What can I do to push myself?".

And make friends. It's a great way to connect with people and make friends. Running with like-minded people of all ages is really good. I really enjoy that aspect of parkrun.

"Just don't say no."

13

Mental health

Mental health problems are a growing public health concern and the enormous scale of the problem worldwide is only just starting to be recognised.

In 2013, depression was the second leading cause of years lived with disability worldwide, behind lower back pain. In 26 countries, depression was the primary driver of disability[27].

Nearly half (43.4%) of adults think they have had a diagnosable mental health condition at some point in their life (35.2% of men and 51.2% of women). A fifth of men (19.5%) and a third of women (33.7%) have had diagnoses confirmed by professionals[27].

Various studies have linked regular physical activity with improvements in mental health conditions and personal well-being, but the general conclusion from many of these studies is that it is more difficult to assess and explain the links between exercise and mental health compared to the links between exercise and physical health.

Nevertheless, there is ample anecdotal evidence from individuals who believe passionately that exercise and being out in nature helped their particular mental health conditions and this chapter highlights two contrasting stories of people who have used exercise to overcome their own personal problems.

Andy has suffered from severe depression and in the interview below explains how his way out of his mental health problems has been a combination of exercise and being out in nature. Andy's story has attracted a great deal of media attention thanks to his high-profile challenge in October 2017.

Sam is a mother from Glasgow who suffered post-natal depression and anxiety after giving birth to her daughter in February 2016. Exercise in the form of running was her way out of this depression.

Here are their stories in their own words.

Andy

What is your challenge and how long have you been doing it?
Challenge is to walk to the top of Ben Nevis, and down again, every day in October 2017.

What motivated you to start?
It comes from the days where I hid away for a year and a half. Three years ago, I was at the end of the world, I couldn't reach further south if I'd tried. I shut the curtains, shut everybody off from the outside world, I just didn't want to know. Then it was when my doctor said I should get outside, anywhere, a park or a hill, and a friend of mine and his partner took me to the Lake District. One afternoon, they literally dragged me

out of the house, because I didn't want to leave. We ambled around and went for a walk, then had a coffee. We had a really chilled out day and at that moment I thought, wow, this is different. This is good, this is good for my mind, and I felt at ease with myself, and I didn't feel the need to hide away in myself. When I was up there I felt like a new person. I could be myself. I didn't have this stigma of all the bad memories of my hometown. So, it was literally the doctor saying, "Get out to the outdoors," and a couple of friends saying, "Come on". That's what started me off. That is exactly what started me off, and it saved my life. I was at the bottom end of the world and I didn't see any way out, none whatsoever. The outdoors just put everything into that little bit more perspective. I think the fresh air helped to be honest.

"My doctor said I should get outside."

What motivates you to continue?
The whole thing now is medication. I took medication for about a year and a half, and it certainly kept me going, as in alive, but it still didn't get me to really want to go outdoors. But I couldn't string a sentence together, because the medication was needed, because it falsely released the endorphins, but then the outdoors took over because it released them naturally. And then it was like, "Ah, this is the feeling of 'better' – brighter shores as they say".

Not everyone is into the great outdoors, some people don't like getting wet through in the rain, unfortunately. That's what this country seems to have a lot of. If you didn't go out when it's raining, none of us would get anything done. Coming back to the getting outside, it doesn't have to be out in the hills, even though that gives a better perspective on you as a human being. Even the park, even the local woods, even the beach. The local pond, go and have a wander down and feed the ducks. Just that atmosphere, as long as you're outside. You start to relax.

This last year, a friend gave up a lot of his time off work to get me into the hills. He'd ring me up to say, "I've got a couple of days off". We'd plan a camping road trip. So, even when I wasn't actually able to get out into the hills, I was still sat at home looking at them. I was planning stuff. I was keeping the mind interested in what I'd seen, so I'd think, "Alright, we'll go here this time. We'll go somewhere different. We'll push the limits a bit, we'll go up a grade."

"Ah, this is the feeling of better – brighter shores as they say."

What difference has it made to your life?
When I was younger I was in the cubs and scouts, so the outdoors was always there, but as you get older your work commitments, family and so on drives you to a life of despair, as I found out. You lose touch with what you used to enjoy doing. Things become unreachable. I used to live in the east end of London; there weren't no mountains there. I live in Blackpool now, it's as close as I've ever been to a mountain. I've got them up the road in the Lake District. I've kind of made it happen that I am in the environment, which is quite a bonus in the end. It's paid off after my own bout of depression. I've discovered the mountains up the road, and everything has perked up a bit. The solution doesn't need to be in the hills, a lot of people get animals to help them out

of the house. You gain a buddy, you gain a mate, you gain somebody you can trust that isn't going to let you down.

"The solution doesn't need to be in the hills, a lot of people get animals to help them out of the house."

What's your message to anyone that isn't taking regular exercise?

I don't want to sound too forceful. I can sit here and say exercise is the best form of everything, but if someone can't be bothered exercising then unfortunately they're not going to get out and do it, but if you're feeling down, the exercise from going down the park and feeding the ducks with the kids. Do it a bit more than you have been doing. Step it up, increase the little bits that you're doing and spend more time outside. The vitamin D in the sunshine, which we don't get a great deal of, is worth soaking up when we do get it.

This sounds harsh. Turn the social media off for a couple of hours during the day.

"Do it a bit more than you have been doing."

Twitter: @mracole1977

Mental Health Information

Did you know that if you text 07725 909 090 when you are feeling really depressed, a crisis counsellor will text with you? Many people don't like talking on the phone and find it difficult to open up to friends and family, or they may not have a support network to turn to.

Some people are just more comfortable with texting.

This is a service run by The Samaritans.

Sam

What is your challenge?

Keeping going. I've always been a bit flakey when it came to taking something up, being dead enthusiastic about it for a while and then it gets dumped by the wayside for various reasons. There was always an excuse or reason why I couldn't keep doing it. So, I'd already tried taking up running a couple of times before. I think it was 2013 that I tried starting Couch to 5K and started doing a bit of running and got into it, then had some issues with my knee, so that curtailed it that time. So I tried again in April/May 2015, then found out I was pregnant, so that curtailed it that time. These are quite obvious things that stopped it, but I am quite bad at sticking at things. I would say my challenge is to keep changing the challenge so that I keep going, so that I'm motivated to keep running, because I have found that I really do enjoy it, I've made a lot of new friends from it. I want to keep going, I don't want to find an excuse to not do it anymore, but I do need to keep changing that challenge to make sure that I stay interested. I do joke with people that I've got the attention span of a goldfish at times and I think that's probably something to do with it. My challenge last year was a Half Marathon and this year I'm working towards the Dublin Marathon at the end of October.

> "I would say my challenge is to keep changing the challenge so that I keep going, so that I'm motivated to keep running, because I have found that I really do enjoy it."

How long have you been doing it?

I started running again properly in September 2016, just

before I went back to work after having my little girl. I needed something that didn't need a gym subscription, didn't need specific timeframes, that I could just do as and when I wanted. So, I picked up the Couch to 5K again and this time it stuck.

What motivated you to start?

I had Eilidh in February 2016, and it was quite a traumatic birth, lots of things went wrong, and ultimately following that I didn't bond particularly well with Eilidh and it led to post-natal depression. I'd never experienced depression or anxiety before, it was totally alien to me. All I knew at the time was that I didn't feel the way that everyone was telling me I should feel after having the baby. Had someone come and knocked on the door and said there's been a terrible mistake, she's not actually yours, I would have handed her over and would not have blinked an eye about it. I could deal with the practicalities of keeping this small person fed, changed, cleaned, watered and able to sleep. Outwardly I was a very good actor, but there's only so long you can sustain that. So, when Eilidh was three months I finally got some help. I say finally, not because there wasn't the help there, but because it took me that long to accept that I needed that. So, I then went onto anti-depressants and went to a peer support group. It took a while, but things started to get better, and I was starting to look towards going back to work in the October. I wasn't feeling great about myself on many levels and a physical level comes into that as well, so I needed to hook into something and I'd seen a few things about running for mental health as well as physical health, and I thought it would be something I could fit around Eilidh and my husband working shifts, so

I could work it around all of that. So, it made sense to give running another go. Yeah, it's definitely stuck this time.

"Outwardly I was a very good actor, but there's only so long you can sustain that."

What motivates you to continue?
Personal challenge I think. When I first started running I used to worry about how I looked to everybody else and that I wasn't faster than other people. When I joined other people for a run the first thing I did was apologise for being slow. I tried to make excuses for why I was doing it the way I was doing it. I've come to realise that doesn't matter. The only person you're running against is yourself. I'm quite happy with where I am now and where my targets lie and what times I can run, when I can push it and when I can't push it.

Actually, the motivation to continue is because I enjoy it when I'm out and it does do wonders for helping you clear your head, and you feel really good that you've done it. Also, I think it's a good positive role model for Eilidh as well. I do parkrun pretty much every week and Eilidh knows all the ladies I've made friends with down at parkrun as well. She comes down and helps me marshal sometimes, she'll high-five all the runners and we go to the park and it's, "mummy run, mummy run". I've got my running gear on and she sees that, and I think it's a very positive thing. She's already decided she wants to do it, and I don't know how she's going to take having to wait until she's four to get her own barcode. But I take her in the buggy sometimes, and I just think for all the negative stuff that happened around her birth and not feeling great about not having that bond initially, it's nice to do something that feels like a positive role model thing for her in her future as well, and she sees me doing it and my sister does it as well.

My sister is a huge inspiration. My older sister was officially known as the non-sporty one. So, there were three girls and Clare was most definitely the one allergic to sport and would avoid it at all costs and never liked doing it. She's the reason I did the Scottish Half Marathon last year, she's the reason I'm doing Dublin and the reason I do parkrun. So, I love it when we go to see her because I get to do a bit of parkrun tourism. It's quite funny speaking to my dad, because my dad goes, "I get you, you're alright, I know why you're doing it, you've always done this kind of thing," but he cannot get his head around the fact that Clare, his eldest daughter who was allergic to sport is going to run a marathon, and is enjoying running and goes to a running club. He's been going on for about two or three years about Clare, and he cannot fathom it. She's a big inspiration in that if she can keep going, and wants to keep going, then I can as well.

"Actually, the motivation to continue is because I enjoy it when I'm out and it does do wonders for helping you clear your head, and you feel really good that you've done it."

What difference has it made to your life?
It's given me something for me. The running is my thing. It's me time and it's brought a lot of different and varied people into my life, particularly through parkrun. The group of people I've met through parkrun are just so lovely and they've all got their own stories to tell. They're so encouraging. We've got someone who is running the Highland Fling on Saturday,

she does ultras, you know, she does marathons like we do 5Ks. And we've got a couple who just turned 70 and we've got another lady who is actually a full-time carer, and her and the youngest lassie in the group are running the Edinburgh Marathon in May, so seeing them doing all their training is inspiring as well. They're just such a lovely and encouraging group of people and so diverse. Yeah, parkrun has been absolutely fantastic for that.

"The group of people I've met through parkrun are just so lovely and they've all got their own stories to tell."

What's your message to anyone that isn't taking regular exercise?
Keep it simple. I think when people think they need to exercise or do physical activity they kind of think too big. They think I need to do this massive challenge, or I need to do something to excess for it to be any good, and actually, you know what, planning a 20-minute walk on your lunch break, every day, that's enough to get you going. It's about finding something that hooks you, that motivates you. Coming from a background of education, we have lots of different learning styles and people have different ways to become motivated. I think some people are motivated by entering a race and having a challenge or something like that to work to. Other people work to numbers, so if they want to lose weight they're going to get to that number and that is going to help them.

So, I think it depends on what your motivation is in the first place, but I think the main piece of advice is just keep it simple. It doesn't have to be complex. It doesn't have to be a marathon or an ultra or big, fantastic challenge that you get sponsored for, it can be one small lifestyle change that can make the biggest difference. Like I say, that might be just building a 20-minute walk into your day, or saying every time we have a day off we're going to do something more active.

"It can be one small lifestyle change that can make the biggest difference."

14

Physical health

Physical health problems come in many different forms and the onset of any new symptoms should always initiate a visit to a doctor for expert examination and opinion. A doctor's diagnosis and advice is of paramount importance in every single case, but the general principle, that the majority of health care professionals would support, is that the correct level of regular physical activity is likely to help in the treatment of most cases.

Physical activity raises our heart rate, encourages the circulation of blood around our bodies and releases beneficial chemicals such as endorphins which make us feel happier and promote our ability to fight disease and develop resistance to infections.

While it is undoubtedly true that prevention is better than cure, at the point where we have a physical health problem, it is too late to prevent it, so our attention turns to seeking a cure. That is the point at which many people look to physical activity to assist their efforts to cure themselves of their physical health problem, however great or small that problem might be.

There are many great stories of people who have come back from some form of illness because of their adoption of an exercise regime to aid their recovery. This chapter looks at two individuals with very different stories, but with a common focus and determination to improve their conditions through exercise and to enjoy themselves in the process.

Chris weighed 27½ stones in 2007 but lost 15 of those stones over a four-year period. His journey from being excessively overweight to cycling across the USA and becoming an honorary Professor of Physical Activity for Health is an amazing story.

Jenny wasn't a runner, but when she was diagnosed with a heart murmur her response was to avoid going down the medication route, and instead took up running, initially through the Couch to 5K Challenge and then parkrun.

Here are their stories in their own words.

Chris

What is your challenge?
Like your own five kilometres a day challenge, my idea has always been just to do something physically active every day. I have a target of making 10,000 steps in a day, but if I don't manage that, I do something, go to the gym, a spinning class, or maybe resistance exercises with weights.

On another level, my life has changed recently because I've just retired, so everything is going to be turned upside down as

I carry on trying to do bits of my old life as a surgeon and all the activities I did around surgery to do with physical activity and promotion of advocacy to do with physical activity. Although now I need to think about other things to do outside my past surgical life. So, that's probably my major challenge at this stage. That's more of a mental challenge than a physical thing, but I suppose my deeper challenge has always been trying to cope with my long-term diabetes and keeping my sugars at a reasonable level and preventing medical complications such as losing limbs, sight and other functions.

So, I think very much in terms of that, and very harshly I suppose, the challenge is also to do with life expectancy. I've just had my 58th birthday and thinking very crudely about life expectancy for the average man, I suppose my life expectancy would have been about 77, and then knowing that I'm a type 2 diabetic would mean that my life expectancy has probably been reduced by seven to ten years, so I might live to be 67 or 70 perhaps, so I suppose in the time that I theoretically have left I need to make every single day count.

"My idea has always been just to do something physically active every day."

How long have you been doing it?

You're always trying to work on your health, but as a young man I was very fit. I was kayaking for Great Britain, I got into white water paddling, managed to go on some big expeditions all around the world, and then I qualified as a doctor in the mid-80s, and I thought I needed to study even more and passed lots of postgraduate exams and became a surgeon and subjected myself to incredible stresses. A lot of that was peer pressure from my colleagues and my father. Trying to impress my father was especially important. Also trying to cope with achieving professionally. During that time I became diabetic and I suppose my health got worse and it was not until my late-40s that I became unwell with diabetes, metabolic syndrome and hypertension, that I finally had to do something about it and had a gastric band fitted in 2007.

So it's really been the last ten years that I've had a major focus on trying to keep my health as good as I can, whilst trying to achieve well professionally, and I think I've excelled in many aspects of that, but it's an unrelenting battle trying to control diabetes. It never goes away. Although when I lost a lot of weight, my diabetes got a lot better and my sugars were virtually normal on no medication. Your insulin resistance gets worse with time though, and I ended up back on medication and developing a neuropathy in my hands, which stopped me doing surgery, and having cataract surgery last year, so it's just a constant battle.

"It's an unrelenting battle trying to control diabetes. It never goes away."

What motivated you to start?
The motivation when I was in my late-40s, when I had my gastric band, was firstly my health. My quality-of-life was so awful, I thought I'd rather be dead, so I thought I better have a gastric band and do something drastic about my weight. But my motivation laid at several other levels and I've thought about motivation a lot. I thought it's probably about wanting to be able to do the things I did when I was younger, because when I was younger I was kayaking at quite a high level and I

was very fit, white water kayaking and running marathons, I thought I'd like to do that again before it's too late.

"It's probably about wanting to be able to do the things I did when I was younger."

What motivates you to continue?

Motivation to continue now is trying to make every day count, and do as much with my life as I can. I'm lucky in that I think I'll have a fairly comfortable retirement with my health service pension, so I just carry on doing the things I enjoy. Carry on cycling, walking, kayaking, doing something every day.

"Motivation to continue now is trying to make every day count."

What difference has it made to your life?

My health problems catastrophically changed my life, but focusing on exercise has been a massive help. Who would have thought that a 27½-stone surgeon would have ended up becoming a professor of physical activity for health? That's just a massive transformation of life roles. In fact, the physical activity job completely took over my role as a surgeon, whilst I was still working in the health service. It did cause some conflict, because I changed my role from a surgeon to a professor of physical activity and my health board didn't really want me to do that. They just wanted me to do clinics and operate and didn't appreciate the leadership I was trying to provide in physical activity.

"Who would have thought that a 27½-stone surgeon

would have ended up becoming a professor of physical activity for health?"

What's your message to anyone that isn't taking regular exercise?

It's a no-brainer, you've got to take regular exercise. There's that cartoon by Glasbergen. It's a cartoon of a doctor and a patient, and the doctor says, "What fits your busy schedule better, exercising one hour a day or being dead 24 hours a day?" It's as simple as that really.

"It's a no-brainer, you've got to take regular exercise."

"What fits your busy schedule better, exercising one hour a day or being dead 24 hours a day?"

Cartoon by Randy Glasbergen

Follow Chris on Twitter: @CyclingSurgeon

Jenny

What is your challenge?

My general challenge is to become and stay healthy. I have a heart murmur, and as a result of that I have put things in place to help me overcome it, because I'm not prepared to give in to medication at all.

At the moment I do parkruns, so my Couch to 5K was a good starting point. I battled with them at the beginning because I'm not a natural runner. I improved week on week with the support of lots of parkrunners. It's such a friendly bunch. I always say that everybody there wants to be there for a reason and they're getting up on Saturday morning to have this run and it's such a wonderful thing.

Every week I've improved, and my mind is set to be sub-30. Now that may not sound very good to anyone else, but to me at 55, with a heart murmur and slightly overweight, it's a good challenge for me. So, I religiously get up and go on a Saturday and do my run. I make friends, I chat afterwards, I listen to advice. There's a great bunch of people there and this week I ran with a parkrunner who had run 250 parkruns and he coached me through the run. The week before last I came in at 36.47 and this week came in at 32.04, being coached by this man. He told me how to run, how to stand, so these are all positive things about parkrun.

So, the challenge for me now is to get to sub-30. When I get to sub-30, it will be sub-29 or 28. What drives me? Just to be healthy and it gives you a focus and a vision.

"I have a heart murmur, and as a result of that I have put things in place to help me overcome it, because I'm not prepared to give in to medication at all."

How long have you been doing it?

I started about 18 months ago, but then I was off for four or five months with an injury. My physio coached me through all of that and told me when I could go back running. Then I slowly came back, and I was devastated with my time when I resumed, so here the challenge comes again. Right, ok, now get below 35 and so on.

I came back in mid-January, so I can run it now without stopping.

What motivated you to start?

I was looking for something that I could do alone, whenever I wanted. So, if I woke up at 6.00 in the morning and couldn't go back to sleep I wanted something to do in the form of exercise. I like being out in the open and I know it's difficult in the winter, but it's nice to be out there in the cold conditions and you get used to it. It's often a mind thing. You put your stuff out in the evening, the alarm goes off, you put your stuff on, you put your watch on and you say, "Right, I'm going". Then you just go. There's no-one stopping you.

So, something I could do alone, something I could monitor myself very closely, without having to check up with anybody else, it was something I could read up on and get information quite easily and then when I was introduced to parkrun, that was like, that's the family. So, I became a part of this bigger family that had the same drive.

> *"If I woke up at 6.00 in the morning and couldn't go back to sleep I wanted something to do in the form of exercise."*

What motivates you to continue?

The results really. The shape of my body. The friendships

that we have. The fact that I'm doing it and finishing it. The determination to get up and do it, because it's very easy to wake up on a Saturday morning and go, "Oh I can't be bothered to go to parkrun," and you could make every excuse under the sun, but on Friday night I'm set up to go. On Facebook, "parkrun tomorrow, I can't wait". Once I commit to something, that's me.

"Once I commit to something, that's me."

What difference has it made to your life?
I would say it's enhanced my path of healthiness, because I've made new friends, I've become healthier and my heart has improved. In fact, my surgeon has said, "I don't know what you're doing but just carry on doing it".

I have a passion within me, when I start something I have to do it to the best of my ability.

"My surgeon has said 'I don't know what you're doing but just carry on doing it."

What's your message to anyone that isn't taking regular exercise?
I have a current objective, a personal objective, to get as many people who are attached to me in whichever way, whether it's work, the village, family, anybody; I talk about it and say this is what it's done for me, come and join me. Not everybody takes it on board, some think it's all about making a massive commitment, but I try to get the message over that it's all about making small challenges along the way. Challenge yourself to do something achievable and you should be rewarded with the benefit of feeling good about the achievement.

I try to lead by example. I feel healthy, I feel happy. I recently said to a relative, "Healthy lifestyle, exercise, good food, fresh air, rest, sleep, holidays, good life, good friends – that's what it's all about". So, I will spend a lot of time with people if they are interested and if I can prove to them what the results are like.

"I try to get the message over that it's all about making small challenges along the way."

15

Prevention (better than cure)

To repeat what was said in the introduction to the previous chapter, prevention is better than cure. For those who hear that and take it on board in plenty of time, there are massive benefits to be gained from being proactive and reducing your risk of contracting a long list of physical and mental health problems before one or more of them have a chance to impact on your life.

The man who lost eight stones then ran the London Marathon in three hours, or the woman who took up cycling following a heart attack and went on to cycle across Canada are the kinds of stories we read about in newspapers and see on TV, because they are *newsworthy*, but the 20-year-old who took up running and cycling in order to have fun and hopefully build her resistance to a hereditary heart condition doesn't capture the imagination in the same way. It just isn't newsworthy. Which is a great pity, because it is a really important story, but at which point do you tell that story? "Forty-year-old woman still hasn't had heart attack following twenty years of running and cycling." As headlines go, that doesn't grab your attention, and anyway, what if she has a heart attack next week?

While not being newsworthy, it is what we should all be doing, or at least what some of us should have done at some point in the past, and that is why this chapter is so important. This chapter is about prevention being better than cure.

Colin had lost the habit of cycling and realised he was missing it, so he decided to do something about it. Getting his bike out of the shed led to him developing an exercise challenge that he now sees as promoting good health and avoiding illness.

Lorna and her partner use their Fitbit devices to track their steps each day and provide them with the motivation to achieve a target figure every single day. They recognised the dangers of leading sedentary lifestyles so decided to take action and now they push each other to keep to their schedule.

Here are their stories in their own words.

Colin

What is your challenge?
It probably didn't start out as the challenge it's become. The challenge originally was just to get back into the habit of cycling, and particularly cycling to work. Something I've done at different times in the past. I've always found it a really good way of getting some exercise into your daily routine. You have to go to work anyway, so by cycling there and back it clears your head, gives you some fitness and it's just a fun thing to do.

So, the challenge has become to try and cycle as much as possible. In terms of work, it's cycling to and from work; if I've got meetings I try to cycle to the meeting, sometimes that may mean taking my bike on the train. If I have a meeting in Edinburgh, I might take my bike into Edinburgh if I have to be there early, but then cycle home, or cycle part of the way home. I just try and incorporate it into my journey and increase my level of active travel; so the challenge has been to get me back on my bike through regular commuting. It's turned into more than what it was originally envisaged to be. I started in the summer, then thought I'd just see how it goes, then the winter came along, and I thought I could get some good lights, which I didn't have, and just see how it goes and keep on pushing it. Then I got some special winter tyres and before I knew it I was cycling, if not every day of the winter, then at least most days. And then six or so years on I'm now trying to cycle every possible day that I can. There are occasions that I don't, but not very often.

"You have to go to work anyway, so by cycling there and back it clears your head, gives you some fitness and it's just a fun thing to do."

How long have you been doing it?
For the last five years I've been averaging about 5,000 miles. I've always been a cyclist, but at times it took a bit of a backseat to being a walker and mountaineer. There have been various times in the past that I've cycled to various places of work, usually in the summertime, but this time for a combination of reasons I've stuck with it during the winter, pushed it as much as I could and thought let's see how we go. Once you've

got one winter under your belt you think, that wasn't too bad, and then the next winter you're even more prepared and determined. So, I just try to cycle in all weathers and just keep it going. If I can do it, then hopefully other people will think they can do it too.

We're all creatures of habit. So, for example, when I get up on a morning I don't think, "How am I going to get to work?" I think, "What am I going to wear on the bike? – What's the weather doing outside? – Do I need to have lots of layers or one or two thin layers?" So, it's about having good equipment and being prepared. I've invested in good equipment, good lights for the bike, winter tyres, and I suppose I have a slightly tenacious streak in my character. Once you've got your teeth into something, it's a challenge to yourself, you think, "How windy can it get before I can't cycle across the bridge?" Sometimes I've had challenges in my life in the past, but it's nice to feel I can challenge myself on a daily basis.

The distance is a round trip of 22 miles. It's 11 miles from home to work, so that's the basic journey. Often, particularly in the spring and summer, I will vary it and do extra loops, sometimes coming in, but particularly going home on a nice sunny evening I might add a few extra miles. It's mainly flat, but a few wee hills. It's more about a steady endurance thing. There have been times when I've pushed it. I've had personal bests on certain sections, but it's really about enjoying myself, it's about having that in my routine every day, and I find it physically and mentally a really good thing, and when I don't do it, which isn't very often, I really miss it.

"It's nice to feel I can challenge myself on a daily basis."

What motivated you to start?

I guess it's a combination of reasons. I'd been meaning to get back into commuting to work. I'd been living further afield, so it wasn't practical. There'd been a number of things happening in my life that had been unsettling, and work hadn't been as good as it could have been. So, for a number of reasons, from a physical point of view I wanted to get back into some regular exercise and mentally I knew it would be good for me, because I'd cycled before. When I moved and ended up 11 miles from work, I thought, "Now is the time" and "It will be good if I can start doing it in the summer," then that ended up just rolling over into autumn and, with good lights and equipment, into the winter.

What motivates you to continue?

The main reason for continuing is maybe partly a stubborn streak. I suppose I wanted to. I suppose I'm the kind of character that likes a wee challenge. It's good to push yourself and it's easy to get out of the habit of having a challenge in your life.

After completing my Munros not long before that, and perhaps subconsciously I was looking for another challenge. It just seemed to be something I could fit into my routine, that was good for me. Also, I always felt I had strong green credentials, I just felt environmentally it was good as well. So, on a number of levels it was the perfect way of getting to work, and see if I could keep it going, and whether it was possible to try to do it, if not every day, then the vast majority of days in the year.

> "It's easy to get out of the habit of having a challenge in your life."

What difference has it made to your life?

Physically, at a time in my life when if I wasn't careful, if I didn't have a regular routine, then maybe I would have started to put on a bit of weight. It's allowed me to keep fit. It allows me to eat that extra slice of cake, if I want to, occasionally. But also, more importantly, I think mentally, in terms of mental health and well-being, it can be really refreshing in a morning just to clear your head, to wake up and be in touch with the countryside, which is what I've always loved doing anyway, and going home in the evenings, instead of something being in your head and going round and round, if something has got in there during the day, it allows it to get out and you don't take it home with you. It gives you that bit of thinking space. And interestingly, I've made friends through it. I now have a cycling mate who I met on the commute, so we now go out cycling occasionally.

"It can be really refreshing in a morning just to clear your head, to wake up and be in touch with the countryside".

What's your message to anyone that isn't taking regular exercise?

My advice to anyone not taking regular exercise would be to realise that just a small amount of regular exercise can be really beneficial. It's not just about the physical aspects, but mentally in terms of clearing your head, being refreshed, it is just so good for you. The more you do, the more you want to do. So, just set yourself a wee challenge that you can keep going and reap the benefits.

"Set yourself a wee challenge that you can keep going and reap the benefits."

Lorna

What is your challenge?
My challenge is to do at least 10,000 steps, every day of the year.

Every single day, and at least, so it has to be walking for at least 10,000 steps. Any other exercise is a bonus.

"At least 10,000 steps, every day of the year."

How long have you been doing it?
For two years, but I stuffed it up last year when I was at a hen-do and forgot to put the Fitbit back on after I was in the hot tub, so I think I probably would have got all my steps that day, but it didn't count because I forgot to put it back on, then the Sunday after the hen-do I just couldn't be bothered and left it at 7,500 steps. I was really annoyed because that was the March, and I'd started in January as a new year's resolution, then I did every other day that year, and then this year I've managed every day up to now (August) and I've managed every single day so far. So, there are no exceptions, it's got to be every single day. I don't have days off.

"There are no exceptions, it's got to be every single day. I don't have days off."

What motivated you to start?
There's a couple of things. One was that I'd managed to put on three stones since moving up here five years ago and that was due to a change in lifestyle because I wasn't walking to the office. I was mainly working from home or driving to another office and not really walking very far, whereas I used

to walk to my office and do a lunchtime walk. I also had a bit of a health scare in that I had a mole that went a bit dotty around the edge and it turned out to be superficial spreading melanoma. They took it out once then had to go back and take out a bigger bit, so it was a bit more frightening. So, there were two things that made me think, "Right, it's about time to be a bit healthier and take more exercise, plus there's heart risk in my family". Both my parents are on heart tablets. So, all that combined made me think I should be proactive, take more exercise and live a healthier life.

> "It's about time to be a bit healthier and take more exercise."

What motivates you to continue?
Because I mucked up on the challenge last year and it was very annoying to miss out by two days, so there's that.

Sometimes I really cannot be bothered if it's chucking with rain or lots of snow, I really don't fancy going out, but I've got to make myself go out or I'll do it in the house, so I do try to make myself go out.

I now know how many steps there are to certain places, so to my partner's work is 1,000 steps each way, because it's just outside the village. So, even if I do it in little bits if the weather is horrible, I'll walk him to his work, come back, walk to the house up the road another 1,000 steps each way. It doesn't take a lot if you do it that way to actually meet the challenge.

> "Even if I do it in little bits if the weather is horrible".

What difference has it made to your life?
It has made a big difference to my life. I did lose three stones, so

I'm a lot healthier now, we've found that we can do a lot more than before. Although it's just walking, I feel that my stamina is a lot better. Definitely healthier and the forcing yourself to go out is very good for you. It gets you out into the fresh air.

"Although it's just walking, I feel that my stamina is a lot better."

What's your message to anyone that isn't taking regular exercise?

I think it's very good to encourage people to do something. It doesn't have to be a challenge as much as 10,000 steps, it could be 500 steps, it could be some other kind of challenge, but to have a challenge is good.

With my work, I've tried to get them to take on the Step Count Challenge and we've done it three times now. There's a spring challenge and an autumn challenge, and although you're in a team it's also your own individual challenge, so it works out the number of steps you took in the first week. It's eight weeks in the spring and four weeks in the autumn. Doing it in the spring puts you in a better frame of mind for heading into the summer and then the autumn challenge is the whole of October, so it's good when Christmas is coming round and everyone is taking in mince pies, so it puts you in a better frame of mind before all that starts. I think it's good to get people out, especially in the winter months when you go to work in the dark and come home in the dark, if they're making that effort to go out for a walk at lunchtime, at least they're out, they're in the light and getting the fresh air – it can only be doing you good.

"To have a challenge is good."

Long-haul flights

A few months after recording that interview with Lorna, I bumped into her and caught up on how her challenge was going. She had just enjoyed a holiday in Canada where she and her partner had managed to keep their 10,000 steps a day challenge going, although they had been concerned about the difficulty of getting their steps in on the day of their return journey. Long-haul flights heading east are a well-known issue for streakers because they not only shorten the day, but for a large part of that day you are stuck inside an aircraft. Lorna's way round this problem, as far as the challenge was concerned, had been to stay on UK-time throughout her time in Canada.

Anyone on a runstreak or exercise streak will automatically think ahead, identify these potential pinch-points and come up with a plan. At least Lorna and her partner thought about it and planned in advance, and didn't have to walk up and down the aircraft aisle as they crossed the Atlantic.

Crossing the Atlantic is one thing, but for streakers, crossing the Pacific is a challenge on a completely different scale. Crossing the Pacific involves crossing the international dateline, and when that is done flying westwards, the result can be missing out on an entire day. A flight leaving Los Angeles on Monday, for example, could land in Tokyo on Wednesday. For the passengers on that flight, it's as if Tuesday never existed, so for the streaker onboard, how could he or she run a mile or get 10,000 steps in on Tuesday? I haven't had to cross that ocean since I started my streak, but if I am ever confronted with that problem, I think I will take a lesson from Lorna and work on UK time, even if it means a couple of boring walks around Tokyo and LA airports.

Walking round and round an airport to keep a streak going might sound a bit over the top to some people, but it is worth bearing in mind the importance of moving on days when you are flying long distances. Long hours spent sitting on planes and breathing recycled air is not good for us, and yet most people in airport lounges pass their time sitting down while waiting to get on a plane. It's little wonder that long-haul flights can lead to serious medical conditions like deep vein thrombosis. The best way to avoid this is to move around the aircraft from time-to-time and to take some exercise (most likely walking) when you are on the ground.

16

Fitness and strength

As with the previous chapter, this one looks at those people taking a proactive rather than reactive approach to their reasons for taking regular physical activity. This time the emphasis is on having a desire to improve your fitness and strength levels as your main reason for taking regular physical activity.

There is perhaps a fine line between the wish to avoid health problems and desire to improve fitness and strength. Indeed, I would have to put myself in both categories rather than choose one or the other. Nevertheless, I've included this category because it is another reason for getting involved in physical activity that is more proactive rather than reactive to some kind of health problem.

The individuals who have contributed stories for this chapter have both taken up running later in life, having spent many years being non-runners. While it is obviously possible to use various activities and sports to improve your fitness and health, these two individuals make some very good points about their motivations and determination to succeed in and enjoy their running challenges. Even if you never go close to running the kind of distances they run, Stuart and

Daile make some excellent comments that you can apply at your own personal level.

Stuart from Glasgow couldn't run 100 metres a few years ago, now he's one of Scotland's most active ultra-distance runners. He describes himself as stubborn, and the fact that he once took a stress fracture 30-miles into a 145-mile race, and went on to complete the run, does support his stubbornness claim.

Daile lives in rural Perthshire and commutes into Perth. We're in the same running club so I've known Daile for a few years. During this time she has taken her running to an amazing level.

Here are their stories in their own words.

Stuart

What is your challenge?
A fairly simple challenge of running at least five kilometres every day.

"At least five kilometres every day."

How long have you been doing it?
My first Runstreak started July 2011 and lasted six and a half years. After a four-week break to have a heart attack my current Runstreak started in February 2018.

What motivated you to start?
It probably started by accident. We'd been on holiday for three weeks on Orkney and Iona, and I'd been running most

days while enjoying the fantastic scenery. Shortly after we got back I did a series of races called the Tour of Clydeside, which is a race every day for five days. When I checked my spreadsheet (yep – sadly, I record every run that I do) I discovered I'd run every day for over 20 days. It felt rather satisfying so I decided to keep it going for a while. I didn't have any sort of length of time in mind. I didn't really set out to do it as a long-term thing but, before I knew it, I'd been running for a year and I just kept going. I had no real reason to stop.

> "I didn't really set out to do it as a long-term thing but, before I knew it, I'd been running for a year and I just kept going."

What motivates you to continue?

Mainly the fact that I enjoy running – and the challenge involved in doing that. I do a lot of long-distance running and have completed the West Highland Way Race four times and Glenmore twenty-four-hour race five times. My daily run has become part of my training.

Before starting the Runstreak I would often find some feeble excuse not to run; it's a bit rainy, it's too cold, I'm too darn lazy! On occasions like that I would later regret not getting out for a run.

If you're running every day, you don't have any option. You get up in the morning, it's raining, so what? You know you've got to run, so you just go and do it.

> "Before starting the Runstreak I would often find some feeble excuse not to run."

What difference has it made to your life?

Running has perhaps saved my life!

I started running when I was 52, so was a very late starter. In fact, I had a non-runstreak for a good 50 years. Managing to not run every single day for all that time was pretty good practice for a Runstreak.

I had been living a fairly sedentary life, and thoroughly looking forward to that slow decline into senile dementia and rheumatism when, one dark night my son and daughter forced me out of my comfy sofa and onto the cruel roads in little more than my underwear. They insisted that I *run* a kilometre – that went well, apart from having to walk 990 metres of it.

But I was a stubborn old bugger, and I would go out at 10 o'clock at night in the dark, so no-one could see me, and I would push and push, and each night try and run a bit further. Every time I went out I always wondered how far it would be possible for someone to run without stopping.

Soon, I plucked up all my courage and entered a 10k race and it built from there. Next came a half-marathon, then a marathon and, inevitably, I was doing ultra-marathons.

My daily running encouraged me to undertake a few adventures including running from the Scottish Borders to the very north of Shetland and running a marathon distance for twenty-six days in a row. To make that more *fun*, I ran from my house to villages starting with the letter A, B, C and so on – X was a tough one!

On the 7th of January 2018 I had a heart attack. At the hospital, the nurse was rather unhappy that I was wanting to pace the ward floor (in an attempt to reach my daily minimum distance) as she tried to connect me to an ECG Machine – at that point I decided it was perhaps time to put the Runstreak, and myself, to bed for a little while. Fortunately my heart was not damaged – four stents were inserted, and I was good-to-go. The neurosurgeons told me that all my running had made my heart strong – so perhaps, had I not started running, the outcome may have been quite different.

The following month I started Runstreak Mark-2 and, with the approval of my neurosurgeon, I ran the Edinburgh Marathon in May and the 95-mile West Highland Way Race in June.

"Running has perhaps saved my life!"

What's your message to anyone that isn't taking regular exercise?

I think you've got to look at why you're not exercising, because no matter what your ability currently is, there's something that you can achieve – whether that's a massive thing like running 1,000 miles or running 100 metres. I came at it from a position where I couldn't run for 1 minute to a position where I can keep going for 20 or 30 hours. I am sure that anyone who is keen can achieve the same or better. Find what's right for you and go and enjoy it. If you're not enjoying it, don't do it. Find something else. You never know – it may even be a life saver!

"Find what's right for you and go and enjoy it."

Daile

What is your challenge?

Challenge is to run 2,017 miles in 2017, and I completed the distance by the end of October. Previous challenge was to run 2,016 miles in 2016. All started with the 2015 Marcothon. I ran every day in December 2015 and then never stopped.

"To run 2,017 miles in 2017."

How long have you been doing it?

I do it on a morning, before my brain has time to register what is happening. Hesitation is the monkey on the back, as they say. So, it becomes part of your routine.

If I had a train to catch at 5.00 a.m. I'd get up at 3.00. Get out of bed, it makes you feel good for the day.

What motivated you to start?

Motivation to start was the Marcothon.

A week or two into it I thought, "Da da, I'm loving this".

Then I was unemployed for a few weeks and running 13 miles a day, so when I started my next job I cut down to ten miles, and that felt so easy. This is only ten miles, I told myself.

Also, I live in the country, so we've got animals around us and this badger hissed at me this morning. Running in the dark can be so nice.

Your mental health benefits go through the roof. You can self-reflect and think about yourself. I've never suffered from poor mental health, although I have an addictive personality. I took up running four years ago and that is what makes me feel good, it doesn't interrupt my family life or personal life. It's added to it. It's made me happier and stronger.

"This badger hissed at me this morning."

What motivates you to continue?
I don't think about whether I can be bothered going out today, I just tell myself, "You're doing this challenge. Get your bum in gear. Get out there and get it done." And then you've done it and you think that was great.

What difference has it made to your life?
It's made me happier, I'm more confident in myself, I know I can achieve more if I put my mind to it and that spreads out everywhere. If I can do this, I can do anything. And the self-reflection, this is my time, it's me-time. I think about whatever is happy in my head – when I finish the run, maybe not at the start of it. But I love it, I feel invigorated.

I used to run to work every morning – 9½ miles. I like a destination rather than an out and back.

"It's made me happier, I'm more confident in myself."

What's your message to anyone that isn't taking regular exercise?
My advice is to just walk to begin with. Maybe start a walking group. Walk to the next stop, but just start walking more.

Then ask yourself, "What do you want to do? What do you enjoy doing?" Just try that. If you don't like it, fine, try something else, but my advice is to make yourself happier. If you find something you like, do it. It will change your life.

Look at parkrun. You can walk it, walk with your dog,

chat at the back, you're not going to be last, just do it. It's getting people to do something once. I wish I could bottle it. It would be the miracle cure. I want everyone to get it.

By the way, we get paid 20 pence per mile if we walk, run or cycle to work. You fill in your expense sheet at the end of the month and you get paid for your active travel.

"If you find something you like, do it. It will change your life."

17

An interview with round-the-world cyclist Mark Beaumont

The ten interviewees from the previous five chapters have inspired me in many different ways, despite the fact that their contrasting situations bear little resemblance to my own. The way my metabolism works, I'm very unlikely to ever weigh more than 25 stones, but I greatly admire Chris' determination to lose weight and take on challenges like cycling across the USA. Similarly, I have been fortunate not to have suffered from the mental health problems experienced by Andy, but nevertheless I found his story fascinating and I have so much respect for the way he turned his life around and what he has achieved.

The stories from Colin and Lorna were probably the two closest to my own experiences. Their stories of reacting to the possibility of their health slipping away from them and deciding to be proactive and take some determined action were really inspirational.

I discussed *inspiration* at the beginning of this book, and reading the ten interviews back has made me realise how the list of inspirational figures in my life has just grown by a further ten. Ten people coming at this issue from ten very different directions, each with an interesting story to tell and each of them an inspiration to other people.

Speaking to each of them left me wanting to discuss this subject with someone from my original list of people that had inspired me to take on my five kilometres a day challenge. We can all be inspired by a mixture of professional athletes and people we know from our everyday lives, so in order to give this section of the book an extra dimension I wanted to capture a view from a well-known athlete to sit alongside the ten interviews from the kind of people we might socialise with or work beside.

I mentioned earlier that I had spoken to Mark Beaumont just prior to his record-breaking round-the-world bike ride. After conducting the ten interviews, I reflected on some of the points about inspiration that Mark and I had discussed, and decided it would be interesting to speak to him again and record an interview for this book.

I had these thoughts and questions for Mark, followed by his own words.

You get involved in world-record-breaking adventures and actively tell the stories about those adventures, but what really strikes me is that you seem to enjoy using those stories to inspire people to get involved in relatively small adventures and activities.

Your cycling round the world seems to be the inspiration for others to go out for a 20-mile cycle ride on Sunday morning or go out as a family to enjoy a short ride, or maybe cycle to work more often.

How much feedback do you receive from people that you've inspired in that way and how do you feel about stories from people who might be doing quite ordinary activities, but nevertheless are doing more than they used to?

I feel quite lucky that my career has spanned the birth of social media. The first time I cycled round the world there was no Facebook. I lived the journey for myself, albeit with a camera at my arm's length, and then only when I came back was it televised and got that public response and I went on a talk tour and I got to meet people. And that was remarkable because I'd no awareness of the wider interest that it could create and what it was like to be in the public eye. It certainly wasn't the reason I got into it. I was the kid that grew up, home-schooled, no television. I didn't grow up saying, "I want to be on the telly," so to suddenly have a public profile, what I call my *virtual peloton*, that global audience around it, is strange to get used to.

But it doesn't matter how many people are following, there's the silent majority who I never hear from, and then there's characters who I get to know very well over the years because they're in constant contact through social media or popping up at events. So, I'm probably talking about tens of people out of tens of thousands, if not hundreds of thousands that follow, who I actually get to know as characters through that following.

Some of them have got remarkable stories. I think people always see that as a one-way street, but it's fantastic to hear their stories and give people confidence to go out and take on their own adventures. I was at an event recently and a lady in her 60s came up to me and said, "I followed your round the world trip every single day on social media and it gave me the confidence to go and strim the nettles in the garden. For years, they've never been tackled, and they've always been a problem and I've always been intimidated by the machinery and just getting out there and doing it. I just want to thank you for giving me the confidence to actually get out there and sort it. It wasn't such a big job, but I've been putting it off for years." Now, it made me laugh afterwards, that she came to my event and felt it important to tell me that I'd somehow inspired her to strim the nettles.

I don't think I inspire people to cycle round the world. I often feel when people feed back to me, that I just give them a bit of confidence to do something that is important in their lives. Something which is maybe not prioritised, or something that they've been putting off. It always amazes me when people come and talk to me at the end of events, they're not talking about me, they're talking about them. They're always referencing their own lives, their own ambitions, their biggest cycle rides and what they've done. So, they're always seeing what I've done through the lens of their own ambitions. I think that's it. I think that's why people follow and why they're interested. They're not interested in what I do in absolute terms, they're interested in me and my journeys and my teams, because it gives them a reference point for their own ambitions.

People always talk about inspiring and helping people. I only hear a few stories, but it's actually a wonderful feedback loop. It works both ways. I've lived through that generation change with social media and when I'm out there pushing myself hard, it's quite incredible to have people commenting, supporting and questioning. Absolutely being a part of the journey. It's not overstepping the mark to say, "Would I keep doing what I do, year after year after year without that public support around what I do?" I don't think I do it for public gratification, but equally, it is a huge part of the fuel in the fire, a huge part of the motivation, the fact that I do get to share it and the fact there is a community who wholly support what I do. I see that as a very positive thing, a very helpful thing, but I don't think that's often talked about. It's just talked about as I'm out there on a crusade and people in some way get inspiration, but I'm very much inspired and supported by them. It's a feedback loop.

There are individual stories which are really important to me. People that have told me it's changed their lives for the better; people who have lost huge amounts of weight or have found travel or found fitness or sport of any ilk. There's a few of them that stand out in my mind over the years. By sharing my adventures, I've in some way fundamentally changed the direction of somebody's life, for the better. That's not the reason you go out and do these things, but I absolutely love that.

"I often feel when people feed back to me, that I just give them a bit of confidence to do something that is important in their lives."

Do you have a daily or weekly exercise challenge when you're not on a major expedition, or is your training more focused on fitness for your next big trip?
Now is a good example, I'm not training for any world record right now, but I have to be in shape. When I'm training for a record, like any professional athlete, I'll be doing 20 to 25

hours a week, sometimes more, but at the moment I've just come back from two weeks filming with CNN. I need to be in shape, I need to be able to turn my hand to lots of different sports and I need that all-round fitness and conditioning, but I don't need to be in record breaking shape. I don't need to have that specific fitness around one sport like ultra-endurance cycling. In fact, it's not particularly helpful to have that. If I had just been trained the way I was last year to race the bike 16 hours a day, that makes you a pretty bad runner, so the things I've been doing over the last couple of weeks have meant a better all-round fitness.

The thing I need to watch very closely when I come off the back of expeditions is my calorie intake, my portion control, cutting down from 8,000 or 9,000 calories a day back to a normal training schedule and diet. Then keeping my upper body strength and core strength, so that I've got that all-round conditioning as opposed to just a specific fitness to do the record attempts.

I typically do a ten-minute core workout every day. It's the same thing every single day. It's a routine. It's simply twice round a four-minute set of 20-second exercises. So, 20 seconds of doing heel lifts, curls, hundreds, planks, walk out planks. 4 minutes of 20 second core exercises, then repeat the round a second time for an 8-minute routine, then 2 minutes of the reverse, so you do things that make sure you're not just curled in, but you're actually stretching out the other way as well.

So, that's a 10-minute routine that I do every single day. Because that's intense, it wakes me up, I can do it anywhere. If I'm in a hotel room or at home, it doesn't matter where I am. I don't need a gym, I don't need anything, it's just a 10-minute blast of 20 second sets wherever I am. I travel so much and don't always have my bike. For example, I didn't stay at home last night, so this morning I got up and did some hill repeats, it only took me 20 minutes, but it's effective training. Even though I'm an endurance bike rider, to do short, sharp sessions which really wake you up and get the endorphins flowing, I find that much more productive than just going out doing long plods.

I think the mistake that a lot of people make is they just go for long, steady rides or long, steady runs. There's a lot to be said for just spending ten or fifteen minutes blasting up and down some stairs or up and down a hill or getting on a bike and doing some intervals. It takes a lot less time, it's a lot more effective around a busy work/life schedule, and do you know what? It has a similar effect. Sure, if I'm doing big endurance events I need to adapt to do the conditioning and ultra-endurance, but a lot of my training is HIIT training. It's half-an-hour, an hour or ninety minutes, whatever I've got, and I achieve good all-round fitness, as long as I do half-an-hour or an hour a day.

I think people assume that being an ultra-endurance rider I simply go out and do long rides. I do very few long rides. I train on the track, I train on the Wattbike, I do a lot of high intensity. You get more bang for your buck.

"I typically do a ten-minute core workout every day. It's the same thing every single day. It's a routine."

What's your message to anyone that isn't taking regular exercise?
I like that great quote, I can't remember who said it, "If you don't make time to be fit, make time to be unwell".

You don't need to be a professional athlete like me, but just look around you, one in two people in the UK getting cancer these days, the issues around diabetes and obesity, and time off work. I just think, why do we have to sell this?

If you've got any wisdom at all, in terms of your longevity and happiness and the impact you have with your family, then our physical and mental health are so important. People don't need to think of themselves as athletes, as long as people realise that physical well-being is absolutely fundamental to our productivity, our happiness and our impact as humans. We're living longer, but are we living well?

It doesn't take that much time every day, it's not about having a phenomenal workout every Saturday morning, it's about the little bits of exercise that we can build into our days. If you don't make time to look after your well-being and fitness, then you're going to have to accept that you're going to have to spend a period of your life unwell. That's the world we live in.

"It doesn't take that much time every day, it's not about having a phenomenal workout every Saturday morning, it's about the little bits of exercise that we can build into our days."

Nettles

The first of ten principles in this book is: "You don't have to copy the person that inspires you. Use your imagination to channel inspiration into your own situation."

The lady who took inspiration from Mark Beaumont

cycling round the world and used it to find the motivation to strim the nettles in her garden must surely win the prize for the most imaginative channel of inspiration into her own situation. Fantastic. What a lovely story and a perfect example of what that first principle is all about.

18

Other inspirational stories

The previous six chapters have looked at the stories of ten people in some detail, plus an insight into the thoughts of Mark Beaumont, so this chapter is going to continue the focus on what other people are doing, only in a more quickfire format looking at what a wide range of people have been up to in recent years.

The same proactive and reactive reasons for taking on an exercise challenge come through in these stories, and there is also a strong element of inventiveness as you read about the imagination and determination that went into so many of these challenges.

Ron Hill

There can't be a more impressive and high-profile example of someone taking regular exercise than Marathon runner Ron Hill. Ron Hill won the gold medal at the European Championships in 1969 and then in 1970 took gold at the Commonwealth Games in Edinburgh. In winning at the Commonwealth Games he became only the second man to run a Marathon in under 2 hours and 10 minutes. He also ran the Marathon at the Tokyo Olympics in 1964 and Munich in 1972.

Long after his international running career ended, Ron was still running ... and running. I think it is fair to say that Ron has always had a love for running. He made the longest runstreak of all time, running at least one mile, every single day, for 52 years and 39 days. That was a total of 19,032 days starting on 21 December 1964 and eventually ending, as it had to do one day, on 28 January 2017. Ron felt unwell while running on the 28th, so he thought it was wise, plus he owed it to his family, to not run on the 29th. The distance he has covered in his lifetime of running is estimated to be around 160,000 miles.

Ben Smith

Ben Smith is the man who ran 401 marathons in 401 days. People thought he was mad, until they heard his story, then they began to understand. Having endured years of bullying as a child, Ben tried to take his own life. In adulthood, Ben struggled to feel content with the life that was mapped out for him, but having found his passion in running, he sold his possessions, escaped his old life and set off on what seemed like an impossible mission – The 401 Challenge.

During his 10,506.2-mile odyssey criss-crossing the UK, Ben ran in 309 different locations, accompanied by more than 13,500 people. He visited 101 schools, burned an estimated 2.4 million calories, wrecked his back and braved every extreme of the British weather, while raising £330,000 for two anti-bullying charities, and touching the lives of millions.

Chris

@Chris_Ball1
This tweet from a chap named Chris sums up what this book is all about.

> 11 months ago I weighed nearly 24st.
> Today I am just over 15st.
> 11 months ago I could barely walk 1km without stopping for breath.
> Yesterday I ran 10km in 48m49s.
> Today I am happy and confident.
> Life is good – it's never too late to change.

Sylvia

In 2015, 85-year-old cyclist Sylvia set herself a challenge[28]. Sylvia had taken up cycling when she was 70 and at the age of 85 decided to see if she could cycle 1,000 miles in a year. She set her target, made her own rules, measured all her rides, succeeded in reaching her goal and raised £1,857 for charity.

Helen

Helen is a retired Geography teacher from Inverness who set herself an ambitious challenge of skiing on real snow in Scotland at least once in every month of the year. Shortly after recovering from oesophageal cancer, Helen set herself this challenge at the age of 55. In October 2019, she reached a significant landmark with her personal challenge: 120 consecutive months, or ten years of an unbroken run of monthly skiing.

While there is plenty of skiable snow in Scotland, and options of where to go to find it in the winter months, there is an obvious challenge of finding snow in the summer. Helen is involved in studying snow patches that last into or right through the summer, so knows exactly where to find sufficient skiable snow. Such patches tend to be found in the Cairngorms, but also around the Lochaber mountains near Fort William. As a result of global warming, such patches have become smaller and less common over the last ten years, so in order to maintain her unbroken run Helen has in some months had to walk up to 9 kilometres to find a patch of snow that was long enough to manage two turns on.

Bob

Bob is an American with a remarkable story to tell[29]. In early 2017, he weighed in at 320 pounds (over 22 stones) and was approaching 50 years old. He was on medication for high cholesterol, high blood pressure and adult-onset diabetes, and there was a family history of heart disease. That is when he recognised the precarious position his life was in, so decided to take dynamic action and started walking 5k a day, which then turned into running 5k per day. Within a year he had lost over 120 pounds. Part of the fun he is having with his challenge is posting silly photos and videos on Instagram.

Oliver

A long-time friend of mine, Oliver, acted as a sounding board as I developed my thoughts and worked on this book. Not surprisingly, the message about the benefits of regular exercise got through to him and he devised his own personal exercise challenge. He came up with a points system, with different forms of exercise having a value, and his target is to achieve 30 points every week. The points system works on one point for every mile walked and one point for every two miles cycled. Other activities like a climbing wall session are worth two points and a day's skiing attracts six points. The maximum score per day is eight points, even if the day's exercise goes beyond eight miles of walking or sixteen miles of cycling. He allows himself days off, but a day off increases the need to score points over the rest of the week. It is very much his challenge, his rules, so he can easily tweak the challenge if he wants to make it easier or harder in the future.

Marjorie

A 92-year-old lady in a care home was inspired by a local community challenge to achieve one million steps each week over a six-week period. She was on her feet at every opportunity and was seen moving around the home with the aid of her frame. The challenge had motivated her to walk, at her speed, and get the pedometer clicking over, rather than sit watching television all day.

Archie

Archie joined his local Walking for Wellbeing group in 2003 after being widowed following 53 years of marriage. His description of life around that time was like living in a black hole, but his way out of that bad place was through joining the Walking for Wellbeing group, making new friends and going out on walks. This eventually led to him becoming a walk leader for the group.

Agnes

An old lady living in a care home was determined to go on a caravan holiday with her family, but that meant being able to climb two steps to get into the caravan. She was so determined to build up her strength and fitness that she had the staff at the home help her with her walking and balance, until she was at last able to climb the two steps. She was then able to enjoy one last holiday away from the home with her family.

Paul

In December 2016, Paul weighed in at 16½ stones, so he worked out that he needed to lose 60 pounds (over 4 stones) to no longer be classified as overweight.

He made a plan to keep to a sensible diet in December and then start with a bang in January 2017. In order to maintain his motivation and keep him on track, he entered six half marathons. He also gave himself a number of other goals for the year.

1. Run all six half marathons in under 2-hours (and run one under 1 hour 50).
2. Run a sub-50-minute 10k
3. Run a sub-22-minute 5k
4. Run 1,000 miles in 2017

By December 2017, he had lost 67 pounds and achieved all his targets. That is an incredible achievement for someone who started out at 16½ stone.

Alain

Alain has an interesting challenge that is well deserving of a place in this chapter[30]. Inspired by the Step Count Challenge, Alain walks the 10 miles to his work every Friday morning.

This means getting up at 4.30 a.m. to make the 2 to 2¼ hour walk to the university where he works. He usually gets a lift home on a Friday afternoon, but during the Step Count Challenge he tries to walk both ways on a Friday in order to give his step count a significant boost.

Babs

Babs needed surgery but was told that she was too big for the operation to remove her gall bladder, so she started walking for exercise. She struggled in the early stages, but built up her strength and now walks from Fife to Dundee and back every day, making the 2.8-mile return journey across the Tay Road Bridge. Her determination has resulted in losing over 10 stones, she has had her operation and made new friends from her regular walks.

John

John is sadly no longer with us, but he did live to a good age and enjoyed a lifetime of cycling. Spurning the often repeated but, some would say, outdated advice to take it easy in your old age, John had a tradition of cycling the number of miles in his new age on his birthday each year. So, rather than cutting down on exercise as he got older, he simply increased the length of his birthday ride with every year that passed.

Rick

36-year-old Rick took on a challenge to run five kilometres every day in 2020 to raise money to help find a cure for brain tumours.

The inspiration for Rick's fundraising came after losing his close friend to an aggressive, grade 4 glioblastoma multiforme (GBM). Danny was just 31 when he died in his wife's arms, after a two-and-a-half-year battle with the disease.

Danny inspired scores of people to raise money for Brain Tumour Research in his honour, through a fundraising page called *Franklin's Star*, set up by his wife.

Rick's challenge highlights another route into taking on a physical activity challenge – fundraising for a cause that you are passionate about.

Pete - Cycling Round the World - Sort Of

This is a truly amazing story from Pete, who set himself the challenge of a virtual round-the-world cycle ride. Here is his story in his own words.

"This challenge grew slowly and evolved unannounced. I moved to Nethy Bridge in the spring of 2004 to start my new job working for the Cairngorms National Park Authority in Grantown-on-Spey. I'd cycled to work regularly two to three days a week in my previous job, but this commute was a round trip of just over 12 miles, so possible most, if not all, days. And so it started.

That first summer, a colleague, Cairngorms born and bred, warned me of the winters to come and "What was I going to do then?" So, quietly and unspoken, the challenge was set; I was going to keep cycling to work regardless of the weather, winter darkness, whatever.

I seldom lacked motivation but, in February 2008, Mark Beaumont set a new record for cycling round the world. My motivation now had a target, I'd aim to cycle a total of 18,000 miles on my *Cycle Round the World to Work*.

The snow-packed winters of 2009/10 and 2010/11 set new challenges and new experiences. Thankfully, I bought some metal studded bike tyres that made my two wheels unbelievably stable and grippy, so much so that some days it seemed to be just me and the snow plough on the road. One memorable blizzard day I made it to the office while a colleague just over a mile away didn't.

By 2014, the end was in sight, so I quietly shared my challenge with another colleague – neither the winter-warner nor the winter-avoider. "Eighteen thousand miles?" he questioned. "That's not cycling round the world; the Earth's circumference is far bigger than that." Protestations about oceans were ignored, so I kept quiet and kept cycling with a new target of 24,901 miles.

Then in 2017 my challenge was hit twice; one amusing, and one frighteningly serious.

Amusing first – without even chatting to me, Mark Beaumont set off again on his second go at setting a new *land record*. He was home in 78 days 14 hours and 40 minutes making my somewhat slower attempt even less impressive.

But three months before he started, I was much more than knocked off my bike at the end of March 2017 by contracting Viral Encephalitis[31]. This is nothing more than cold sores in the brain but incredibly uncommon and potentially life damaging. Thankfully, Lorna, my wife, and NHS Raigmore in Inverness spotted I had something worse than my usual hypochondria and I was treated so quickly and so effectively that my brain damage was *relatively* small.

Three weeks in hospital on a drip and the virus gone along with some of my brain function. Then home to recover and rebuild my damaged brain and to learn anew how to love and appreciate family and friends. After much persuasion of my HR colleague, and for me and no-one else, by week five I was back in work and cycling ... cycling round the world.

All is anecdote, but those who know me believe my exceptional and ongoing (and still challenging) recovery from Viral Encephalitis has been so good because of the support of family, friends and colleagues AND my slightly obsessive round the world cycle.

So, on Thursday 24 May 2018, I finally made it round the world, a mere 5,069 days slower than Mr Beaumont, but I did the wet bits too. I tweeted ironically that day comparing our adventures and Mark *Liked* it. I also had a nice supper and the next day I started my second circumnavigation, on the road to Grantown."

A recent conversation with Pete revealed another bizarre challenge he had taken part in. As part of an Australia Day celebration he did a headstand and someone said, "I bet you can't do one of them, outdoors, every week, for the next fifty weeks and provide photographs to prove it". Always one for a challenge, the bet was agreed and fifty weeks later, Pete won the bet. During the fifty weeks he learnt that the Gaelic phrase for upside down is *bun-os-cionn* (bottom above head), so he dubbed it the Bunoscionn Challenge.

Carla Molinaro

In the summer of 2020, Carla Molinaro broke the world record for running the length of Britain from Land's End to John O'Groats. Shortly after completing her epic run, Carla posted this inspirational message on her LEJOG World Record Attempt Facebook page.

CHALLENGES!

I have had a few people message me saying that they have just completed a challenge, but it doesn't even compare to mine. BUT IT DOES!

It doesn't matter how big or small your achievement is. What is important is that you have set yourself a challenge and you are on your way to smash it or maybe you have achieved it already. And what may seem small to one person is huge to someone else!

You should take the time to celebrate what you have achieved and be proud of what you have done. Don't think "I've only done a 5km and so-and-so has done 100km so mine doesn't count". It totally counts and we are all on our own journeys.

Be proud of what you have done and shout it from the rooftops!

That's a truly humble and inspirational message from someone who took on a monumental challenge that most of us couldn't even begin to imagine.

A massive well done to all the people mentioned above. The world is full of people like these, stretching their imaginations and setting their own personal challenges. The human spirit is alive and well, and I just love hearing and sharing these wonderful stories.

PART 4

More Challenges

19

The Daily Mile

Can you remember your former schoolteachers by their favourite catchphrases? I can remember a few of them. One in particular sticks in my memory. My woodwork teacher's catchphrase was, "The essence of design is simplicity". I liked that phrase for its, well, ... simplicity.

Returning to the subject of regular exercise, if I had to choose one initiative that stands out above all others as making the greatest contribution to tackling the problems of inactivity, obesity and poor health, it would have to be The Daily Mile. The essence of its good design is in its simplicity, even though it has nothing to do with woodwork.

The Daily Mile was the idea of Elaine Wyllie when she was headteacher at St Ninians Primary School in Stirling, Scotland. Here is Elaine's own description of The Daily Mile, taken from The Daily Mile[32] website:

"Until recently, I was the Headteacher of St Ninians Primary School in Stirling, Scotland, where I was concerned about the lack of fitness displayed by the children. I decided to do something about it and founded The Daily Mile in February 2012.

The Daily Mile has a simple aim – to help children get fit by running or walking for 15 minutes a day in school or nursery. The Daily Mile began with a one-month trial and (overnight) the results were startling. While many children could not initially manage the one-mile run, within four weeks almost everyone was able to and just as importantly, the children enjoyed it!

By September 2012, the whole school was running for 15 minutes each day and not one of our 57 Primary 1 children was deemed overweight by the school nurse. Attention levels and behaviour in class improved and parents said that their children are fitter, more active and alert. I was overwhelmed by the level of support that we received from parents.

I've now retired from teaching and am dedicating myself to introducing The Daily Mile to schools across the UK, to help tackle our growing childhood obesity and physical inactivity crisis and to improve the physical, social, mental and emotional health and wellbeing of our children."

The simplicity of The Daily Mile comes from the fact that it involves the two most simple forms of exercise, walking and running. Simple as that, just going for a walk, or speeding it up a bit and going for a run. The combination of movement and fresh air is what the human body craves. Rather than suppressing that simple human requirement, The Daily Mile provides it on a regular, daily basis. What's not to like?

After recording my interview with Sean, the teacher from Chapter 12, I asked him if he had a regular slot in the day when he took his class out for their Daily Mile or whether he varies the timing. He came out with a really interesting reply. He told me that he always does it at the start of the afternoon session, when the kids come back from their lunch break, because that is when there are lots of emotions going on. After lunch and the extended playtime there are some kids coming back inside angry, while others are upset or anxious, so the physical activity involved in walking or running a mile acts to neutralise all those emotions and settle them down for the afternoon. Also, now that Sean is able to run with his pupils on their 3-lap mile, he observes them on the first lap then on the second and third laps he runs alongside anyone that he notices having an issue. He says it is so much easier to run with someone for a minute and have a chat with them to find out what the problem is, as opposed to trying to have that kind of conversation in the classroom.

With teachers like Sean seeing real benefits from The Daily Mile and expressing their enthusiasm for it, it's no wonder that it is catching on and spreading all around the world. As of July 2020, there are 11,193 schools in 78 countries that have adopted The Daily Mile, and that figure is only going to grow.

Now, imagine if all primary schools were to adopt The Daily Mile, and imagine if it were to be introduced in every secondary school, and imagine if every pupil that participated in The Daily Mile at school were to challenge themselves to keep walking at least a mile on at least five days a week after they leave school. That would make an enormous positive difference to the health of millions of people around the world. There's a lot of imagination in that sentence, but The Daily Mile really does have the potential to be one of the major initiatives that could help resolve this problem. And all because one primary school headteacher was concerned about the fitness of her pupils and came up with an idea to address the problem. What an idea. What an absolutely fabulous idea.

If you do one thing today, walk (or run) at least one mile.

Even if you're an adult, don't let the kids have all the fun, go out and walk (or run) at least a mile. It will make you feel better.

Or why not go one step further and introduce The Daily Mile at your place of work or study. Consider this example: in May 2018, the University of Dundee introduced its version of The Daily Mile for staff and students[33]. So, an idea that started in a primary school looks set to spread to other sectors and other age groups. Fantastic!

20

Parkrun

Parkrun is a worldwide phenomenon. You may well have heard of it.

It's hard not to hear about it these days. It's often mentioned on television news programmes, it's in the newspapers and you may well see it happening if you're around a park on a Saturday morning.

Parkrun is a series of free, weekly, five-kilometre runs/ walks, held on Saturday mornings. The first ever parkrun was in Bushy Park in London, in October 2004. 16 years later, there are 1,850 parkruns and over 350 junior parkruns in 22 countries around the world. New parkruns are starting up almost every week, so those numbers are constantly growing and making any printed figures, such as in this book, increasingly outdated.

Parkrun is all about getting out there on Saturday morning to run, or walk, five kilometres. Junior parkruns, for four to 14-year-old children are two-kilometre runs on Sunday mornings.

There are many aspects of parkrun that I absolutely love to bits, and one of the main ones is that it appeals to such a broad spectrum of people. Just stand at the finish line and watch everyone finish a parkrun from the first runner in well under 20 minutes to those running or walking across the line at the tail end of the field, probably in somewhere over 50 minutes. The runners at the front are top club runners, even Olympic athletes, but as the minutes tick by and the runners get gradually slower, the body shapes change, and the average age rises. Nevertheless, the passion for parkrun remains the same throughout the field. Everyone has their own story and their own reason for going to parkrun. Everyone has a target, whether it's to get under 17 minutes, run 100 parkruns, aid recovery from illness or injury, lose weight, make new friends, just get out of the house or any one of an endless list of other reasons. There are millions of parkrunners and thousands of reasons for running them. As a friend of mine put it, "Parkrun has managed to hit the spot, it really has been the right thing at just the right time".

Parkrun was founded by Paul Sinton-Hewitt who surely can't have imagined the scale of what he was creating when he organised that first ever parkrun in 2004 and 13 people turned up to run.

All these years later, Paul has written the foreword, or "pre-event welcome" for the *Parkrun UK: 2017 Run Report*[34]. This annual document is a really good read, because it contains so much information around what parkrun is all about and what it has achieved. I would like to quote two very special paragraphs from Paul's foreword.

"During my travels it was wonderful to meet so many amazing folk and see the way the parkrun concept has been embraced all over the world. I will never tire

of hearing how parkrun has inspired people to make a positive change in their life or how it has helped to unite a community. But what really has the most profound effect on me personally is meeting parkrunners who were previously inactive – people who thought that running wasn't for them, who believed organised physical activity was daunting or inaccessible, who didn't realise that walkers are not just welcomed at parkrun but they also get the loudest cheers. It's these parkrunners who embody what our movement has always strived for: personal empowerment."

"In 2017 we continued to redefine what it means, and looks like, to be physically active. The average finish time at 5k parkruns in the UK was 28 seconds slower than the previous year, and more than 50,000 people who took part identified themselves at registration as being inactive, clear evidence that we continue to be viewed as a first step to a more active lifestyle."

The parkrun website at www.parkrun.org.uk is an incredible source of statistics. Have a browse around the site sometime and you will discover the level of detail about the many parkrun events and the achievements of the participants. Their analysis of the times that people have achieved allows them to come up with all sorts of interesting facts and figures, like the fact that the average time taken to complete a 5k parkrun in the UK in 2017 was 28 seconds slower than in 2016. Yes, that's right, average times are getting slower and that is actually good. It means that parkrun is attracting slower runners, people that haven't run for many years, older people, people that walk rather than run and people that have realised that however slow they go they won't come last. There is always a dedicated tail walker at the back of the field, so no matter how slow you are, there will be someone behind you. So, don't hold back, get along to a parkrun and help make that average time even slower over the coming years.

If you do want to start going to parkruns, then all you need to do in advance is register via the website and print out a copy of your bar code. Then, you turn up at any parkrun event, run or walk the 5k and show your bar code to the volunteer with the scanner at the finish line. Once you've been to a parkrun and seen how easy it is, then looked up your result online, you will almost certainly want to go back and do it all again, and again. To register, go to www.parkrun. org.uk, click on *Register* in the top right-hand corner of the screen and follow the instructions from there.

While you're on the parkrun website have a look at the blog section; there are some thoroughly inspiring stories written by people with an interesting tale to tell about why they go to parkrun and what they get out of it. I visit the blog on a regular basis because I enjoy reading those stories and gaining an understanding of the reasons people have for going, and the uplifting benefits that so many people are enjoying from their Saturday morning exercise.

When you read articles in the media about parkrun, a lot is made about its positive contribution to the health and well-being of the nation. *Health and well-being*, now there's a well-used phrase that we probably don't stop to think about. We probably hear someone say, "Health and well-being" and think they just said, "Health". So, what do we mean by *well-being*? The meaning of *health* is fairly straightforward, but what difference does it make when we attach *and well-being* on the end of it?

In 2016, Paul Sinton-Hewitt gave what I consider to be one of the best television news interviews I've ever seen[35]. The news item was about the 1,000,000th parkrunner, and Paul was asked about the benefits people gain from parkrun. Here is the response he gave:

> *"I think the next ten years is going to see the real impact that parkrun has delivered to changing the well-being, not just the health, but the well-being of the nation. We're helping people come out of their houses who are lonely. We're helping people who have weight issues. We're helping people who have mental issues. This is a fundamental part of changing the nation."*

That emphasis on well-being, and the founder's ability to express the range of issues within its meaning, is one of the great attributes that has helped parkrun to become such a great success. Its contribution to the mental health, as well as physical health, of its participants has been phenomenal. On another level, it is just great fun, and the atmosphere is always so relaxing and welcoming.

My local parkrun is in Perth (the Scottish one). After completing the Perth parkrun one Saturday morning in summer 2016, I was chatting to a friend who was there with her cousin. The two women in their early 50s had just run their first parkrun and proudly told me they had completed it in 39 minutes. I congratulated them and expressed my hope that they would come back and run it again soon. I went on to say, "You'll be surprised how much quicker you'll be next time.

I bet you'll go two-minutes faster if you come back next week."
I heard afterwards that as they walked away, one of them said,
"That bloke must be absolutely barking if he thinks I can run
round there two minutes faster than that". Well, they came
back the following week, took just over two minutes off their
times and their conversation went something like, "Wow, that
friend of yours really knew what he was talking about. I can't
believe we were so much faster, and I don't know about you,
but I feel less tired than I did last week."

As well as running the Perth parkrun on a regular basis,
I've also got into what is known as *parkrun tourism*. That's
the name for visiting other parkruns away from your local
event. At the time of writing, I've run 134 parkruns, which
have included 38 different venues. Wherever you go in
the country, the atmosphere is the same, one of support,
camaraderie and fun.

Parkrun has also broken new ground in that there are
now weekly events being held in the grounds of over 20
prisons in the UK, and prison parkruns have spread to other
countries. In terms of preparing inmates for release back
into society, providing opportunities for healthy exercise and
volunteering, and delivering an activity with a genuine sense
of achievement, the introduction of parkrun into prisons has
been a great success.

Don't just take my word for it that parkrun is the best
thing since sliced bread, here is a recent tweet from Jo Pavey,
European 10,000 metres champion in 2014.

*"parkrun is just the most amazing thing! In terms of
getting people active, it is simply incredible! It's so positive
& inspirational…and it happens every single weekend!"*

Here is a poem and couple of powerful stories from the parkrun blog, which give a flavour of the inspirational comments that people have been making about parkrun and the variety of impressive reasons they have for taking part in parkrun.

I LOVE parkrun by Scott Leach

I love that everyone is welcome. I love that at my first parkrun there was a 30+ stone man working really hard to improve his health. I love that Jonathan Brownlee holds the course record at York. I love that there are kids with their parents and dogs with their humans. I love that I can use it for rehab after an injury. I love that there is often cake. I love that I have an exclusive card that gives me access to hundreds of events the world over. I love that anyone who wants it can have that same access. I love that people happily volunteer to be VI guides. I love that I paced my friend to her first ever sub 30 time. I love having a profile with all my stats. I love that I can run a course of any kind: grass, tarmac, mud, hills and every combination of the above. I love that I can run them around lakes, coastlines, castles, stately homes, housing estates, sports fields, a ninja turtle shaped-park and other countries. I love the shirts that I am working to earn. I love staying with my camera until the final finisher to make sure everyone gets a photo. I love that there are people that only volunteer and don't run because they know how special it is. I love that there are so many people so dedicated to their parkruns and I love that there are people that only go tourist. I love that it's free. I love being able to race and get a time. I love that there are people as happy to break

50 minutes as 20 minutes. I love the diversity. I love that we all get to share it together. I love Saint Sinton-Hewitt for having set this all in motion and keeping it on the right path. I love that toddlers mix with teens that mix with the middle-aged that mix with the elderly, and I love that every one of them is a parkrunner. I love that people walk and wheel and limp and sprint and smile at parkrun. I love that former Olympic athletes take part. I love buying a bacon sarnie and mug of tea in the sports association after the run and chatting to everyone and I love that the money goes towards the sports association. I love the marshals that cheer me on. I love a PB. I love a milestone.
I love the parks
I love the running
I LOVE parkrun!

A bit of explanation:

Olympic triathlete, Jonathan Brownlee, held the course record at the York parkrun for over five years, although his time was eventually beaten.

VI = visually impaired.

The shirts = Parkrun milestone T-shirts = Free T-shirts that you can claim when you have run 10 (under-18s only), 50, 100, 250 and 500 parkruns. There is also a milestone T-shirt for those who volunteer their time to help at 25 parkrun events.

Lake = English word for a loch.

Tourist = Parkrun tourist = Someone who travels to run in different parkrun venues.

PB = Personal Best.

So excited for my year ahead[36]

Photo courtesy of Val Lovatt from VLPhotography.co.uk

"I love this photo of me at parkrun. For someone with low confidence to love a photo of them where there are jiggly bits, sweat, no makeup and no posing is highly unusual – but this is now my Facebook profile picture and I share it with pride. It shows the joy and sheer happiness that I have discovered thanks to parkrun, and it shows Jarrod my tail runner that day who stayed with me the whole time and who I now consider a friend."

Few photos in parkrun history have been shared on social media more times than this image of Dawn Nisbet at Oldham parkrun.

With record numbers of parkrun first-timers taking part at the weekend and New Year's resolutions in full swing,

Dawn explains the story behind the photo and reveals her hope that it will inspire and motivate other people to make positive changes in their lives.

In April 2016, a very close family member was diagnosed with ovarian cancer. Feeling very powerless to help or do anything I decided to do the Pretty Muddy Race for Life[37] planned for July, that way I felt I was helping and doing my part and showing my love.

My cousins sadly lost their grandfather to cancer around this time, so we signed up to the Race for Life as a team to support each other and hopefully have a little fun along the way. I have to add that at that point I was very overweight, completely inactive except walking my two dogs and at the point where any exercise was difficult and not fun at all. Being so unfit and unhealthy, my opinion of self was low which limited a lot of my activity and self-confidence.

Over the next few months we trained (mostly in the evenings under the cover of dark). None of it was pretty, although somewhere along the way I noticed I started to enjoy the mostly walking with a little running and a lot of sweating. I noticed also that my sense of pride through achieving what I had thought was the impossible was improving and my self-confidence that each day I was going out and proving myself (and others) wrong was rising in leaps and bounds. To cut a long story short, we did the race in July and had such a laugh, although the mud did linger a little.

A couple of weeks before the race I realised that once I had completed it, with nothing to aim for it was highly likely I would stop running and revert to my old unhealthy ways where I had no pride in myself, and really didn't want to do that.

A colleague at work mentioned 'parkrun' to me. I'd never

heard of it before as quite frankly it's not something I would have ever considered as for me. I researched it on the internet and sent an initial email to Oldham parkrun which is local to me to test the water – I think if I'm honest I was hoping they would say "no you're too slow and don't run the whole 5k so thanks but no thanks" which would have meant I had tried and it wasn't my decision not to go.

But they were wonderful, so welcoming, happy for me to walk the whole thing or whatever suited me. They explained about the tail runner always being last and staying there if I needed them. They even told me the name of the tail runner the week I planned to come so I could look out for him, and the name of the Run Director so again I could say hi!

So, the first Saturday after the race I went to my first parkrun. I went super early and was really nervous. I said hello to the run director and then just sat on the outskirts, watching lots of runners who were super fit and who obviously knew each other really well.

I did feel scared as I couldn't see any particularly overweight runners. Then I found my tail runner 'Tom' and said how nervous I was and how slow I was and I wouldn't stop saying sorry to him for having to stay with me. Every time we passed a marshal I apologised for being so slow – but they all smiled and cheered me on.

Tom was a lifesaver and just talked to me the whole way around, running with me when I wanted to and walking with me too. Don't get me wrong – it hurt and I did cry – but the determination to prove I could do it spurred me on. I don't know where this comes from as when I look at my 18 years of inactivity, giving up on anything difficult or challenging was a common theme.

I made it! I was so slow and everyone else had finished but there was a cheer from the remaining runners and volunteers as I passed the finish line. There was no smile that day or arms in the air as I was crying so hard from pride that I had done it, and probably also a bit of pain and panic as I tried to catch my breath as a sprint to the finish was in order.

'That' photo of me smiling was taken during my sixth parkrun and I love it. For someone with low confidence to love a photo of them where there are jiggly bits, sweat, no makeup and no posing is highly unusual – but this is now my profile picture and I share it with pride. It shows joy, it shows Jarrod my tail runner that day who stayed with me the whole time and who I now consider a friend (and who has since offered to pace me to improve my time even though he is one of the fastest runners at our parkrun). I know a few people have seen my picture and the general comments are that it shows the joy, sheer happiness and pride that I have discovered thanks to parkrun.

I would love for my photo to encourage anyone considering joining parkrun by showing the community that supports such a great event and the inclusivity to all, regardless of age or ability. And every time I look at my picture I know I can do anything I set my mind to and I inspire myself, which is an amazing place to be. I have two daughters and I hope that they see their mum going out and achieving her goals and I hope this inspires them to be the best they can be and to never give up, even when it seems really tough and to be proud.

I volunteer regularly at parkrun to pay back to those who have helped me so much. We never leave until the last runner/walker has finished. It doesn't matter how fast you do it – 5k is still 5k. Don't get me wrong, I am still slow and it's still tough, but when you're the final finisher you get the biggest cheer. Now I've done a few, other runners smile and say hello and I have met some friends there too.

During 2017 I aim to cover 500k in total, which means lots of parkruns. I am so excited for my year ahead!

Dawn Nisbet

Transformations are possible[38]

Will Roberts tells us what it is like to receive a type 2 diabetes diagnosis, how diet and exercise has helped him to reverse his condition, and asks you to just imagine what is possible.

It's 30 January 2016 and my GP has just told me that I have type 2 diabetes. It's not a surprise given my weight, so I ask "How do I get rid of that then?". The discouraging answer is "You can't. We can only manage it". I left the GP's surgery clutching a prescription for Metformin. I hate taking any medication and have just been told I would have to take it for the rest of my life.

Research on the Internet returned Dr Michael Mosley's *The 8-week Blood Sugar Diet*[39]. I ordered a copy. Instead of taking the Metformin, I bought a blood glucose monitor and started following the book. Within two weeks my blood glucose levels were back in a normal range and by the end of the eight weeks I had lost two stone. And after four months, I was three stone lighter than at diagnosis and as far as I was concerned had reversed my type 2 diabetes.

This is all very well, but I still wasn't doing anything to improve my fitness...

Picture a 64-year-old man who has never taken part in sport, even as a child. He is still about three stone overweight and a 20-yard dash is the limit for him.

My wife and daughter suggested I join a running group, so I booked a place on a course organised by Redway Runners in Milton Keynes. The promise was that at the end of 10 weeks I would be able to complete a parkrun. Fat chance I thought! After the first run which lasts three minutes, I was wheezing and knackered... but I managed to keep up. And two days later I was pounding out a run on my own. Another couple of days and I was out there again. What is going on?

After three weeks I could run without stopping for ten minutes. Not only that, I began to enjoy it and the prospect of running parkrun became a real possibility. But in week six, the excruciating pain in my knee stopped me in my tracks. It felt terminal! My run leader, Portia at Redway Runners recommends a local physio. One miracle later and I was back.

A Saturday morning in Milton Keynes... This man who ten weeks previously had done no exercise in his life is about to set off with over 500 others on a timed course of 5k. It is (of course) my first parkrun! A practised runner was alongside to pace me. After 4k my legs told me that they can't continue. I accelerate! Across the line and I lean over, my jelly legs are struggling to support me. It feels great! In that moment I was determined to run 10k and wondering what it would take to run a marathon. It seems that transformations really are possible!

Thanks to Portia Simond for being an inspirational course leader. Thanks also to the rest of the group for the support. Finally, it was my running buddy, Sam, who got me round on the day. I'll be looking out for you all every Saturday at parkrun.

I'd say to anyone living with type 2 diabetes to look at nutrition and exercise. What works for one, might not work for another, but experiment and don't give up. As for exercise, parkrun is just brilliant! Completing 5k is a hugely rewarding achievement. It is difficult to avoid making new friends at parkrun. And if you see me out running or at parkrun, please stop me and say hi.

Will Roberts

21

Other popular challenges

The Daily Mile and parkrun aren't the only events and challenges that are getting people out there in their droves to become more active.

Appendix 1 lists a number of other fun ways that have been devised to get more people, more active, more often. It is perhaps obvious to state that this list does not include every initiative taking place around the world. There are bucket loads of them out there, so the list in this book is just a small sample of the many organised ways of getting folk off their sofas and out their front doors.

There are many others that I haven't heard of and lots more that are yet to be launched. Perhaps you might take an idea from the list in Appendix 1 and develop some kind of initiative yourself. You could, for example, instigate something along the lines of Healthier Fleetwood in your own area or suggest some type of Step Count Challenge in your workplace.

The list of initiatives might just give you some helpful ideas.

22

Active commuting

Yes, this is a book that is dedicated to promoting physical exercise, and yes, I can hear some of you screaming out that you don't have the hours in the day to take that exercise. I also hear some of you begging me to stop banging on about finding time, because you just haven't got any spare time. Well, here's a solution that could be a neat Win-Win.

It's called Active Commuting.

¿Qué?

Active commuting is the simple act of travelling to and from work using the power of your own body. So, rather than using your car or public transport, you walk or cycle to work. Or you can run, kayak or ski if you have the energy and the appropriate workplace, but let's focus on walking and cycling.

What's more, this kind of commuting can also save us money. You might be short of time for exercise, but I bet you would appreciate a way of saving some money to spend on other things.

Active commuting has been described as the ultimate form of multi-tasking and physical activity through the backdoor. You're travelling to and from work anyway, so why not take some time to analyse your journey options and be imaginative in terms of how you might build some active commuting into your journey.

A lot will depend on the distance from your home to your work. If, for example, you live 50 miles from work, you're probably not going to walk or cycle the whole way; not every day anyway. However, you may work out that you drive 50 miles each way and pay £5 to park your car each day, but you might have the option of driving 49 miles, paying £2.50 a day for parking and walking a mile each way to get to your work. You could save money on fuel and parking, build some exercise into your journey and arrive at work having calmed down from the stress caused by driving. That could be called a *double benefit*. An initial challenge could be to do that at least 100 times in the next year.

Another example could be someone who travels five miles by bus to get to and from work and the bus might drop them off 200 metres from their place of work. That could amount to them walking 400 metres in the day, or around five or six minutes. Over five days, that's not going to mount up to 150 minutes of exercise for the week. However, there might be the option of getting off the bus a mile from work and being able to walk across a park to get into work. That could result in walking ten miles per week and delivering more than the recommended 150 minutes of exercise per week, plus the bus fare might be a few pence cheaper for the shorter journey. Another double benefit. If that scenario could apply to your commute, then why not encourage someone else travelling on the same bus to walk with you?

Remember that daily routine in Chapter 4: *The chair*? Even in that scenario of a daily pattern of car, bus or train commuting, working at a computer all day and sitting watching television all evening – a walk from car, bus or train to office and back again of 15 minutes in each direction would result in a weekly total of 150 minutes of walking. You're commuting anyway, and the last part of a car or bus journey is often the slowest because of town or city centre traffic, so it makes sense to use your imagination, consider your options and think of an alternative that could result in you introducing an active travel element into your daily commute. And think about the double benefit.

Many of us now work from home or take the odd day out of the office to get some intensive work done at our home computers. I started working from home a few years ago and was offered a useful piece of advice from a friend. His suggestion was to build a commute into my day, by leaving the house each morning after breakfast, walking for a few minutes before arriving at my work, and then reversing the process in the afternoon, thereby leaving work, walking and arriving at home. As well as helping with that switch from home to work mode, and back again, it also ensured that I got some fresh air and exercise, which meant that I arrived at work feeling more awake than I would have done if I had just had breakfast then slumped in front of my desk. If you're a home worker, just try it and see if you notice the difference. You can vary the length of walk you take each time and mix walking and cycling to give yourself a bit of variety.

If you're the boss man or woman, you could use your imagination to come up with ways of incentivising active travel. Remember Daile's comment about being paid by her employer to walk or cycle to work. Could you adopt that kind of policy within your organisation or actively promote the Cycle to Work Scheme[40]?

Parking as close as you can to your workplace is likely to become a thing of the past. In contrast, active travel is very much the future. It doesn't involve getting into sport or even getting dressed up, but it might require a bit of imagination to think through your options.

Another form of regular journey that is often made by car, is the short, repeated trip to friends, relatives and shops within a mile or two of our homes. While walking is the most commonly used form of transport for journeys up to one mile, the car is more than twice as likely to be used for journeys between one and two miles in length[41]. Many of these journeys could easily be made by walking or cycling, providing valuable exercise, saving the cost of fuel and reducing carbon emissions. For someone who drives a short distance most days to see their parents, or drives a similar distance to the shops, then a simple challenge to begin with could be to make that journey on foot or cycle, four times a week.

So, while parkrun or a workplace challenge might be the route into a more active lifestyle for many, leaving the car at home and walking half a mile each way to see their parents might be the main opportunity for others to achieve some much-needed exercise that will take them beyond the recommended 150 minutes of moderate exercise per week.

Appendix 2 contains an open letter, dated 9 April 2018 and addressed to the four transport ministers in the UK. This letter is included to highlight the complex issues surrounding the promotion of active travel and the political changes and commitments that are required to bring about a change in attitude towards children actively travelling to and from their schools and an increase in parents' confidence to allow their children to travel to school on foot and bike instead of by car.

23

Workplace activity

Inactivity in the workplace is the scourge of the modern age.

Have you noticed how we often look back at previous eras and wonder, "How did we ever do that?" Whether it was working with asbestos, going into stinking, smoke-filled pubs, driving around without wearing seatbelts or operating machinery without the kind of guards and eye protection that we now take for granted.

These improvements have been the result of a concerted effort to raise standards in a wide range of health and safety arenas. Whenever a new piece of health and safety legislation is passed, it is all too easy to think, "That's it, we've arrived, we've finally sorted everything". Well, of course, we haven't sorted everything, and we should guard against complacency. However, compared to the 1960s when I remember growing up with regular news of accidents to people at work and on the roads, we've definitely come a long way, but we need to constantly question, "What next?" and keep pushing at the boundaries.

There are plenty of areas to analyse and consider for making further improvements to health and safety regulations, but the prime one in my mind is to seriously address the culture of inactivity. It may be true that, while we are sitting at a desk being inactive we are unlikely to be hit by a vehicle or entangled in rotating machinery, but we are in severe danger of being slowly, excruciatingly slowly, overtaken by some form of physical or mental illness. Employers need to take this issue seriously and have genuine concern, plus a responsibility and duty to ensure that their workers move more and sit less. A particular job may be wholly based at a desk, but if that is the nature of the employment on offer, the employer should have a level of responsibility for ensuring that the employee's inactivity is balanced with a corresponding level of activity. If that sounds radical, well so did the people who campaigned for mandatory wearing of seatbelts and banning of smoking in public places.

Accidents can happen in a split second, and accidents that can be categorised can be addressed, and the likelihood of them being repeated greatly reduced. When I was about seven, a man in our village fell from height at work and was left partly disabled for the rest of his life. The type of working at height regulations we have today would have made his job safer and prevented that accident from happening, but it took accidents like that to create the political pressure to persuade politicians to act and bring in legislation to protect workers. In this case, the need to improve the *safety* of workers was obvious. Other risks to workers take longer to show up as a serious health issue, a classic example being asbestos, which people worked with for many years before the risks were fully understood and legislation brought in to protect future workers from what became recognised as a terrible danger to health.

Inactivity in the workplace is another form of industrial risk, just like working at height or handling asbestos. Jobs are becoming more sedentary and we now have a pretty good understanding of the health risks that this poses to those working in these mainly indoor jobs. The problem is that inactivity is in the slow-motion, long-term health hazard category, rather than a quick, violent, short-term accident, so it is a harder concept for the political system to tackle. But, tackling it is something that governments, employers and society must do.

Given the urgency to address this issue, here are a few suggestions for encouraging a workforce to be active, motivated, healthier and more alert for their sessions at work.

Standing desks

If the biggest problem in the modern workplace is too much sitting down in a position that is bad for our skeletal posture and blood circulation, then the most simple and logical solution is to stand more and sit less. The most obvious way to achieve that is to stand up at our desks. So, a big well done and pat on the back to the inventor of the standing desk. You might think that the inventor of the standing desk is a living person that came up with the idea around about the millennium, but the person responsible is far older than that, given that Leonardo da Vinci and Sir Winston Churchill are reported to have been supporters of working on their feet rather than backsides.

Standing desks are becoming more widely used and proving to be increasingly popular. However, there is disagreement about their health benefits, so it can't be claimed conclusively that they are proven to be a solution to all the problems associated with sitting down at work. Research points to health problems with too much sitting and too much standing. On that basis, and at least until such time as we have more conclusive evidence, it is up to the individual to look at the advantages and disadvantages, try a standing desk for a trial period and come up with your own conclusions as to what works best for you.

Given that there are health risks associated with *too much sitting* and *too much standing*, a balance of some sitting and some standing throughout the working day would seem to be a better combination than all of one or all of the other. I certainly favour the alternate pattern of one-hour sitting, followed by one-hour standing, repeated through the working day. Most standing desks can be moved up and down, so you can find the optimal combination of sitting and standing throughout your day.

Did you know?

- Denmark became the first country, in 2014, to legally require employers to give workers the option of having a standing desk.
- While not going that far, Australia and Canada have taken on proactive campaigns to encourage employers to create healthier work environments.

Walking meetings

A walking meeting is pretty much self-explanatory. Rather than sitting on opposite sides of a desk to speak with someone at work, a healthier alternative is to go out for a walking meeting. The walking meeting has its limitations, in that it is only really feasible with groups of two to four people, where there is a suitably quiet and peaceful place to walk and when the weather is conducive to being able to walk comfortably and hear each other speak. Can you imagine having a walking meeting against a backdrop of city centre noise and interruptions from charity fundraisers or while being blown and battered by a winter gale? However, a walk in a park or rural location, on a calm, dry day, can sometimes lead to a more productive atmosphere than the conventional meeting room. I can't imagine a walk in the park becoming the alternative venue for the board room meetings in the TV programme The Apprentice, but in situations like meeting with colleagues, especially where there is an element of creativity required or a preference to reduce the level of formality, then a walking meeting can be an excellent alternative to another hour of your life spent sitting in a chair.

Deskercises

From tapping your feet under the desk to standing up and running on the spot every 30 minutes, deskercises (or desk yoga) are exercises designed for performing at office-based workstations. Type *deskercises* into a search engine and look at the range of exercise routines that come up. There are some great ideas out there and they can make a worthwhile contribution to reducing the negative effects of sedentary working. However, and this is a massive HOWEVER, it requires determination, devotion and commitment to keep on doing your deskercise routine. To really make a difference, you need to devise a deskercise routine and do it every hour, of every day, for the rest of your sedentary working life, not just twice a day for the next two days. In my view, the best way to achieve the required level of commitment is for employers to actively promote deskercise routines and make them a mandatory part of working for that organisation. That kind of approach might go some way towards reducing an employer's liability, should illness caused by sedentary work ever become a basis for legal challenges.

Lunchtime

Dare I mention lunchtime routines? Do you do lunch al desco or al fresco? In other words, do you have lunch at the desk while continuing with your work, or do you go out for a walk? I'm sure you know what's coming now. If you're an al desco person – how can you treat your body like that? Are you under pressure from your boss to work such a solid stint and be there to take phone calls with your mouth full of egg mayo sandwich, or under pressure from yourself to condense your hours into the shortest time possible? Either way, having lunch at your desk without having a break from your work is a bad habit to get into. If this applies to you, then please have a think about it. It is a habit, a bad habit, and one that you should avoid getting dragged into, and need to quickly break out of if you already do it. I should know – I used to do it.

This is the UK Government advice on the law relating to breaks at work, "Workers have the right to one uninterrupted 20-minute rest break during their working day, if they work more than six hours a day. This could be a tea or lunch break.

The break doesn't have to be paid – it depends on their employment contract."

A 20-minute break is the minimum that anyone should be taking. For people in sedentary jobs, an opportunity to stand up, walk around and get away from their desk, preferably to go outside, has to be seen as a vital part of their day. One way to improve your lunchtime routine is to set a measurable target. Here are a few suggestions:

- Go outside every lunchtime.
- Find a space and do five minutes of stretching every lunchtime.
- Walk a total of one mile in your lunchtimes each week.
- For those working in tall buildings, walk up and down 30 flights of stairs during your lunch break each week. For example, walking from the 10th floor to the 16th, and back down again, each day. If anyone on the intervening floors asks what you're doing up there, just explain your routine. With a bit of luck, your idea will catch on and you will have the satisfaction of having inspired someone to take more exercise. Can you imagine how great it would be if all the workers in an entire skyscraper full of offices took on the challenge of walking up and down 30 flights of stairs each week? The Daily Mile for tower block workers! The distance covered might not be great, but climbing stairs is a quick, exercise snacking way of raising your heart rate.

That's just four quick suggestions to get you thinking. Over to you now. You can have fun coming up with your own challenges and building them into your daily routines.

Promote active commuting

There is nothing quite like a cash incentive to influence behaviour. The story of Daile's employer paying their staff 20 pence per mile to actively commute is a perfect example of this. As well as saving money on fuel or public transport, an actual payment of cash means that people working there can earn money from their daily commute rather than it costing them money. "Sign me up please." Are there any more employers out there willing to follow that lead?

Even if you aren't in a position to get paid for actively travelling to work, you can still save money and gain all the benefits from the exercise if you cycle, walk or run to work. Active commuting, as previously explained, is an effective form of exercise, because you're travelling to and from work anyway, so rather than investing time and money in a sport, you use time that was set aside for commuting in any case to cycle or walk instead of *sitting* in a car or bus.

Another, more complicated, phrase for this is NEAT, or Non-Exercise Activity Thermogenesis. NEAT is the energy expended for everything we do that is not sleeping, eating or sports-like exercise. It therefore includes the energy used walking to work, performing our work, cooking our meals, operating the TV remote and so on. As a somewhat extreme example, it is easy to see why a ski instructor will have a higher NEAT than an office worker. This explains why NEAT could be a crucial factor in how we maintain our body weight and/or develop obesity or lose weight. The study of NEAT is a complex area of physiology but, rather than trying to understand it, it might just be better to raise our NEAT by being more active, especially in our commuting.

Drivers

If you drive for a living, then all this advice about standing up and taking breaks is going to sound like $e = mc^2$. Taxi drivers, bus drivers, lorry drivers, sales representatives and countless others that drive for most of their working lives are going to be in that dreaded sitting position for several years of their lives without the opportunity to stand up every hour on the hour, or every time the phone rings or to go through a deskercise routine when their on-screen alert reminds them to do so. Current regulations state that a goods vehicle or passenger-carrying driver must take a break or breaks totalling at least 45 minutes after no more than 4 hours 30 minutes driving.

For the person in an office job, 4 hours 30 minutes is likely to be more than half a day's work. For anyone in a non-driving job, imagine sitting down at 1.30 after your lunch break and not standing up again until 6.00, and having to maintain a high-level of concentration for that entire afternoon shift. That is what some people are doing to earn their living while others are sitting at desks or chopping down trees. Work comes in all kinds of formats, but driving is the one that stands out as requiring the longest spells of sitting down without easy opportunity to stand up and move about before resuming work again. It also stands out from the point of view of the large numbers of people that are employed in that sector. I can't think of any other profession that involves so many people in such a sedentary role.

The main EU rules on driving hours[42] are that you must not drive more than:

- 9 hours in a day – this can be extended to 10 hours twice a week

- 56 hours in a week
- 90 hours in any 2 consecutive weeks.

So, a long, but legal, day can be two 4 hours and 30 minutes shifts with a 45-minute break in-between. That is a lot of time spent sitting in one position. Up to 9 hours sitting in a 9 hours and 45 minutes working day. Now, be honest, would you want to go for a run or a bike ride after that kind of day-at-the-wheel? I have to say that I really take my hat off to any driver that recognises the importance of regular exercise and sets themself an exercise challenge. However, for the majority of drivers who aren't meeting the recommended targets for exercise, this really is a priority group of workers whose profession is likely to impact on their long-term health and who need help in counteracting their time spent sitting down.

Workplace challenges

A great way of becoming more active via the workplace is to take part in a workplace challenge. You could organise a challenge yourself or take part in one that a colleague or sports and social committee is setting up. The list of challenges in Appendix 1: *Other popular challenges* provides a wide range of suggestions to choose from.

Workplace challenges can be great fun and provide the initial stimulus for many people that get into taking more exercise, as well as bringing colleagues together to share an informal bonding experience that can have considerable benefits for the employer as well as employees.

The good news is that workplace challenges are becoming increasingly imaginative and popular. Up and down the country, employees are loving the activities, the challenges, the camaraderie and, importantly, the health benefits that are flowing from such initiatives.

Advantages of an active workforce

There is no doubt in my mind that any employer will be rewarded with a range of benefits from having a more active workforce.

The following information is taken from the Healthy Working Lives[43] website.

Evidence suggests that physical activity can benefit an organisation because active workforces tend to:

- report less illness and recover more quickly from the illnesses they do get
- experience less work absence*
- experience lower staff turnover
- be more productive
- have fewer industrial injuries
- report higher levels of satisfaction with their work
- create a positive corporate image.

* According to the Physical Activity Task Force, 2003, physically active employees take 27% fewer days of sick leave. This equates to over two days' improved attendance and a saving of £135 per employee.

What can employers do to promote physical activity?

Employers can promote and encourage increased levels of activity in a number of ways.

It is recommended that employers develop an organisation-wide plan or policy to support employees to be more physically active.

Suggestions on how to achieve this include:

- Encouraging employees to walk, cycle or jog part of or all of the journey into work. This can be encouraged in a number of ways, such as by offering secure cycle parking, developing a travel plan and providing information on, and actively promoting, local walking and cycle routes.
- Allowing staff to work flexible hours that can accommodate physical activity, such as longer lunch breaks.
- Joining a corporate membership scheme with local leisure services and promoting this with staff.
- Encouraging participation in local and national events such as sponsored walks and fun runs.
- Arranging a team gathering or corporate away day that involves some form of physical activity that most staff would be able to participate in, such as a short organiser-led walk.
- Encouraging the use of stairs by displaying the Healthy Working Lives stair walking posters.
- Arranging a corporate challenge, with prizes or incentives, that involves physical activity. For example, assigning staff into teams to compete to see who can walk/jog/run/swim/cycle the most miles in a given time period.
- Providing staff with information on the benefits of physical activity and asking them what types of activities they would be interested in participating in.

24

Or, get a dog

Any dog owner reading this is probably wondering what all the fuss is about. Most dog owners go out to walk their dog at least twice a day and some have probably been covering at least five kilometres per day for far longer than I have. We're a nation of dog lovers and we know how much our dogs enjoy, and require, a good walk or run. However, we sometimes overlook the wide range of benefits that dog owners receive from owning a dog. Not only do dog owners benefit from the physical activity involved in walking, and in most cases achieve over 150 minutes of exercise per week, but they also enjoy the more hidden benefits including:

- Reduced stress levels
- Relief from depression
- Easing of loneliness and isolation
- Lower blood pressure
- Increased likelihood of interacting with other people
- Added feeling of safety when out with a dog.

There are thousands of dog owners out there who walk a

certain distance every day, in all weathers and without any kind of exercise plan in mind. With the exception of the dog owners who make their dog run behind their car, the vast majority of dog owners are some of the most active people in the country when it comes to time spent on their feet and moving about.

However, dog ownership comes with responsibilities and it is not appropriate for everyone, and you certainly shouldn't go out and buy a dog just to force yourself to take more exercise. Owning and caring for a dog is something you should give serious consideration to before going out and choosing any kind of dog. Here are a few questions you will need to ask yourself to determine whether you are suited to owning a dog:

- Do you have previous experience of owning or looking after a dog?
- Is your lifestyle compatible with having a dog in your life?
- Is your living space suitable for sharing with a dog?
- Can you afford all the costs associated with looking after a dog?

If you live in a small city-centre flat, and spend your days out at work, and evenings socialising with friends, then you probably don't have the space in your flat and time in your day to offer a dog a decent quality of life.

You also need to be aware of your legal duties as a dog owner and not allow it to chase farm livestock, and prevent it from chasing other animals onto roads. The owner of a dog is legally liable for any damage caused by their dog, such as dead sheep and the results of any road accidents. For the sake of the dog and the people, animals and property that it could damage, do not take ownership of a dog if you aren't willing to face up to that level of responsibility.

Another aspect of dog ownership that is worth considering, especially in relation to ways of the human owner taking more exercise, is to compare the options of buying a dog or an exercise bike. Other exercise machines (rowing, running, etc.) are available. Here are a few advantages in favour of the exercise bike over the dog:

- You don't need to arrange for someone to look after your exercise bike when you go on holiday.
- You don't need to take your exercise bike outdoors several times a day, every day, year after year.
- You don't need to buy special food to feed your exercise bike.
- You don't need to pick up poo when your exercise bike squats in the park.
- You don't have to pay expensive vet bills when your exercise bike develops a fault.
- Your exercise bike won't lick your face immediately after licking its rear axle.

Then again, in favour of owning a dog, these are the advantages over the exercise bike:

- The dog will accompany you on a wide range of outdoor adventures and get you out on cold, wet, windy days in winter, and beautiful sunny evenings in summer.
- The dog will thank you with its unconditional love and enthusiasm, just for being there to share the adventure with it.

- The dog will savour the afterglow of being outdoors and fall asleep with its head on your lap after you get back home.
- The dog will teach you that weather is irrelevant and that just getting outdoors is what really matters.
- The dog will occasionally lick your face with that lovely, sloppy tongue.

Given all those considerations, if you do decide to buy a dog, the next issue becomes what kind of dog you would like. Which breed of dog do you have a passion for and how will that fit into your lifestyle? For example, you might want one of the breeds known as a toy dog, such as a Pomeranian or Chihuahua, but from an exercise point of view a toy dog might get you out for short walks, but it isn't going to join you for long walks or adventurous runs in the forest.

If you are genuinely a doggy person and want a dog that will become your "running partner that is always there," then a Labrador, spaniel, collie, greyhound, whippet or similar, is likely to make a perfect partner for you and become a companion to share some great times with. It needs to be a two-way relationship though. You need to be right for the dog, and it needs to be right for you. When there is a perfect fit in each direction, the result can be truly life-enhancing for the owner and their dog.

If you are in the position of looking for a dog, then you might like to consider providing a loving home to a rescue dog. Rescue dogs make great pets and are deserving of a second chance in life. There are lots of organisations out there providing re-homing services for rescue dogs. The Dogs Trust, Border Collie Trust and Labrador Rescue Trust are just three of these charitable bodies. An internet search should lead you to other organisations in your local area or specialising in other breeds. While some internet searches will lead you to genuine organisations offering useful services, beware of the recent trend in unscrupulous puppy farms selling unhealthy puppies that have been bred in horrendous and cruel conditions.

Another factor that does need to be considered when thinking about dog ownership is the life cycle of the dog. A puppy needs to be introduced to the world gradually and carefully, and its level of exercise built up as it becomes bigger and stronger. Then a young dog will go for long walks and there will be times when you might struggle to give it sufficient exercise, such will be its enthusiasm and energy for running around; but as the dog ages you will find that the walks get shorter and slower, and the exercise you get from dog walking will also diminish. You might even need to compensate for the shorter, slower walks as your dog gets older and get outside by yourself to ensure you still get some meaningful exercise. Sadly, and inevitably, old dogs die and leave their owners bereaved. There is a true saying about owning a dog, and that is they bless you with the happiest days of your life, and one of the worst days. After losing an old dog, many owners will get straight back in there and find a new puppy, and suddenly the walks get longer and faster once more, and the life cycle of the dog goes around one more time.

The chapter on exercising with a dog wouldn't be complete without a big shout-out to all the hard-working assistance dogs. Some dogs have real full-time jobs to do, as opposed to part-time jobs like digging. Assistance dogs perform a really wide range of tasks now and aren't confined to being guide dogs for the blind. There are now hearing dogs for the deaf, medical detection dogs and assistance dogs for those with disabilities. These specially trained dogs provide valuable companionship as well as increasing people's independence and confidence. They also require their own exercise and encourage their owners to take exercise, despite whatever their personal difficulty might be.

If you do take your exercise with a dog, then enjoy every minute and reap the many benefits of going out walking and running with your special friend.

Further information

The Kennel Club[44] website is an excellent place to visit if you are looking for information on finding a dog and considering the responsibilities of owning a dog.

For anyone looking at running with their dog, the Canicross[45] website is a great place to go to for information about this fun and increasingly popular off-road running sport.

There is also Bikejor[46], if you want to be dragged along by your dog(s) while you ride your bike.

25

Sleep, hydration, exercise, diet and stretching (SHEDS)

This is a book about the benefits of regular exercise, but this chapter looks at the other aspects of a healthy lifestyle – sleep, hydration, diet and stretching. Make improvements in each of those areas and you are likely to feel some really positive benefits to your health.

I will stress again, this is a book about the benefits of regular exercise, so I won't go into the other aspects in anything like the same level of detail as I have for exercise. There are plenty of books and websites out there on each of these subjects, and I would certainly recommend to anyone that they read around these aspects of a healthy lifestyle, analyse what you read, think about what works for you and then make a real effort to implement some positive changes in each of these areas.

From my experience, if you take one of these aspects seriously and spend some time thinking about it, then you are likely to be drawn towards thinking about each of the others.

If you keep thinking and learning about SHEDS (Sleep, Hydration, Exercise, Diet, Stretching) and keep making improvements in each of those areas, then you are likely to be making the best possible investments in your future life. Try this for yourself, and I hope you find yourself on an upwards spiral. Think of SHEDS as a five-pronged attack on unhealthy lifestyles.

Have a picture of some sheds, and whenever you look at that picture, think about Sleep, Hydration, Exercise, Diet, Stretching and how you could do something today to make an improvement in at least one of those areas.

Sleep

Sleep is the means by which our bodies recover their energy supplies and repair damaged tissues. The quality of our sleep is reduced by a range of modern-day issues such as a sedentary lifestyle, television, computer and mobile phone screens, stuffy bedrooms, and work and financial stresses.

You should seek help if you are not sleeping well. Don't just put up with poor quality of sleep; mention it to your doctor and try to get a solution based on an improved lifestyle rather than resorting to medications.

Our bodies try to repair themselves when we are asleep, and the better we sleep, the more our bodies are able to carry out those repairs. I sometimes suffer in the winter months with the ends of my thumbs splitting. Something I've noticed over the years is that these cracks in my skin always heal well during a good night's sleep. I wake up after a poor night's sleep and the split skin is still there, and might even be worse than the previous day, but wake up after a good night's sleep and it tends to be better or even healed completely. Something as simple as a skin condition can be improved by having a good sleep, and a couple of contributory factors in that quality of sleep can be taking some outdoor exercise the previous day and not looking at a screen in the hour or two before going to bed.

Another trick I use if I'm not getting to sleep is to not just lie there. If I've been lying awake for over half an hour I do something. I either get up and go to the toilet, or read for a while, or on most occasions I do both. More often than not, that break in the monotony of just lying there seems to work and I usually get to sleep when I turn out the light.

There was a night a few years ago when I had woken up and just couldn't get back to sleep. It was about 3.20 a.m., around mid-summer. I went to the toilet and realised that I just didn't feel tired. So, I went back to the bedroom, got dressed and went out for a five and a half kilometres walk, then came back to bed and slept like a log. In the morning I told my partner that I'd already done my 5k. She asked how I'd done that, so I said I got up at 3.20, walked 5.5k, then came back to bed an hour later. "I didn't even know you'd been out of bed," she said (she doesn't have much problem sleeping).

Hydration

Our bodies are approximately 60% water, but we are constantly losing water via sweat, breathing, urine and bowel movements. That water needs to be replaced by drinking and eating foods with a high water-content, such as fruit and vegetables.

Thirst is our automatic reaction to dehydration, so we have an inbuilt mechanism telling us to drink when our body needs it most. However, there are times when we might not be feeling particularly thirsty, but we might still be slightly dehydrated. Our fluid needs vary from one individual to another, so it is difficult to give hard and fast guidance, but it is often felt that most people don't drink enough to stay optimally hydrated.

It is claimed that energy levels and brain function are affected by dehydration, and runners and other sportspeople are advised to maintain their hydration levels and not wait until they are feeling thirsty. I know from my own running that I need to take plenty of fluid onboard before a run, keep drinking during longer runs, and then keep replacing lost fluids after running. I remember the days before I learned about the importance of hydration, when I used to finish a long run and get a thumping headache. I couldn't work it out at the time but looking back now it was caused by dehydration. I'm glad to say I don't make that mistake anymore.

Not surprisingly, exercise and heat lead to an increase in our throughput of water, mainly via sweating and our increased breathing rates. We therefore need to take this into account and drink more when we are in a warm place (overseas holiday or hot summer's day) or taking exercise that gets us hot and/or out of breath. If as a result of reading this book you plan to increase your levels of exercising, then your body is likely to churn out more fluids and therefore need to replace them. You are going to need to drink more water. Also, consider that you might not have been drinking enough to begin with, so you might need to increase your intake by more than you think.

When I decided that I needed to drink more, I adopted two simple actions. I now have a drinks bottle beside the bed and the first thing I do when I get up on a morning is take a few sips of water. Then I have a one-litre drinks bottle on my desk and make sure that I drink at least one bottleful during the day. Also, if I'm out for the day, I have a one-litre bottle with me at all times so that I can maintain that plan to drink at least a litre of water during the day. From my own experience, I tend to find that I feel more awake when I'm well hydrated. Dehydration can lead to drowsiness and lethargy, so it is important to drink plenty of water when performing tasks where drowsiness could be dangerous, for example driving and operating machinery.

Our fluid requirements depend on a number of factors including our age, health, living and work environment, activity levels and so on, so it is difficult to give a recommended daily amount to aim for. Two litres or eight times an eight-ounce glass are sometimes quoted, but that is just a general ballpark figure. As well as getting into the habit of drinking plenty of fluids, it is also important to think about when you are likely to need more than normal and to avoid getting thirsty in the first place. It is also worth being aware that hot drinks and fruit juices count towards any target that you might set for yourself.

It should also be stated that it is possible to drink too much water, so don't read this and think I'll just go over the top and drink loads more than I do at the moment. There is good information out there (including NHS[47] and Health Line[48] advice) and I would encourage you to look into the subject, because good hydration is an important aspect of a healthy lifestyle.

Just like building exercise into our daily routine, with a bit of thought and planning it is easy to build hydration into our routines as well.

Exercise

The rest of this book is about exercise, but I include it here to contribute the letter E in the spelling of SHEDS.

Diet

There is a massive amount of information out there on diet, and a lot of it is contradictory and at times controversial, so I don't want to get involved in those debates. It seems that whenever one study says that (pick one from the following list) coffee, cheese, olive oil, red meat or red wine is bad for you, another study comes along saying it's good for you. I'm not a doctor, so I can only look at the reports on these studies and make my own judgements, much like you probably do. I'm not, therefore, going to state my views on the pros and cons of the various food debates.

However, a good diet is the basis of a healthy life and we should all be paying attention to the quality of our diet and giving thought to what we eat and drink. What doesn't appear to be in any doubt is the value of fresh fruit and vegetables and the recommendation to eat at least five portions of fresh fruit and vegetables every day.

So, to keep it simple and offer some general advice, I would suggest:

- Consume at least five portions of fruit and vegetables every day.

- Think about your diet, seek good quality advice, learn about food and find what suits (and doesn't suit) your body.
- Keep thinking about ways to improve your diet.
- Avoid so-called junk foods.
- Don't be afraid to reverse out of cul-de-sacs. If you made a change to your diet and subsequently think it hasn't worked as expected, then change it again.

Five-A-Day is great advice, but have you ever wondered how big is a portion? After all, a single grape surely doesn't count as one of your five. Just so you have the definitive guidance, those all-important guidelines from the NHS are shown in Appendix 3.

A word about junk food

Of all the health-related issues discussed in this book, from childhood obesity to reduced life expectancy, the two major contributors are lack of exercise and poor diets. A powerful phrase that I heard on the radio recently was, "We have to change our relationship with food". The speaker went on to say, "Exercise alone isn't the key to losing weight".

Just as it has become too easy to jump in the car and drive half a mile to the shops instead of walking or cycling, it has also become far too easy to fill our stomachs with food and drink that contains little in the way of our real dietary requirements and everything in the way of excess sugar, salt, saturated fats and profits for the companies producing such junk.

Governments are beginning to talk tough in terms of suggesting there is the political will to show some public-sector leadership in tackling this crisis, but so far it appears that lobbying from large, vested interests in the food and drink manufacturing industries is still preventing initiatives like sugar taxes, a ban on 2-for-1 offers and tougher food labelling from being properly implemented.

In the meantime, it is up to us, as individuals and families, to raise our awareness of what is junk and what is good, and make every effort to improve our diets to as healthy a level as possible.

A phrase that should be stuck to your fridge door is, *You can't outrun a bad diet.* In fact, do it right now, write or print, **You can't outrun a bad diet** on a post-it note or piece of paper and stick it on your fridge door. It will act as a timely reminder – several times a day.

Salt and sugar

Two of the biggest offenders in terms of dangers to health in processed foods are salt and sugar. To learn more about the dangers posed by these two overly-used ingredients, I would recommend visiting the Action on Salt[49] website and Action on Sugar[50] website.

I would also recommend anyone wishing to improve their diet and relationship with food to read the article: *We're in a new age of obesity. How did it happen? You'd be surprised.* by George Monbiot[51]. This lays out a very clear argument about the way in which excess sugar has been loaded into our diets over the last 40+ years.

The main thrust of this book remains focused on the need to find time for exercise, but we also need to ensure that we have no time for sugar, salt and the processed food industry that has so far succeeded in exploiting every opportunity to pile these ingredients into our diets.

Stretching

Our joints and muscles were designed for moving us around, but we increasingly seem to use them for maintaining a stationary slouched sitting position. We need to give them a damn good stretch at least once a day – preferably more. So, use it or lose it, seems to be the commonly accepted advice.

As well as taking exercise in the form of walking, running, cycling and maybe some sporting activity, we also need to stretch our spine and move the muscles that are designed to maintain the spine in its intended shape. As I've already stated, this is a book about regular exercise; it's not a yoga or back care book, but stretching should be seen as part of the overall package of measures to improve our health and lifestyle.

There are plenty of good books out there, plus personal trainers, osteopaths, physiotherapists and other back care specialists, all of whom can offer advice on a range of simple exercises to increase your suppleness and help you maintain better posture.

For anyone who doesn't currently take the time to perform some stretching exercises, I would recommend finding at least five stretches that you can learn and perform on a daily basis. Don't just make up these stretching exercises yourself and don't do any that force your back or joints to bend too far. Bending over to touch your toes is not a good exercise, especially if you are not a naturally flexible person.

A site that I can recommend for anyone looking for a useful range of basic stretching exercises is the British Heart Foundation YouTube channel. The following two videos on that channel demonstrate some simple stretching exercises: "Strength and flexibility exercises"[52] and "10 minute living room workout"[53].

I've developed my own workout routine during the time I've been working on this book. These lines from the interview with Mark Beaumont have really stuck with me, "I typically do a ten-minute core workout every day. It's the same thing every single day. It's a routine." Those three sentences inspired me to develop and incorporate a 10-minute workout into my daily routine, so I now have my own version of Mark's workout that I build into every day. As well as finding time for my at-least-5k-journey, I also find time for a 10-minute workout built around stretching and strengthening my core muscles.

Marginal gains

A concept that coaches in elite sport often talk about is the *Aggregation of marginal gains*. They work on the basis that if you find ten actions that will each knock 1/100th of a second off your time for a particular event, then you should save 1/10th of a second in total, and that might make the difference between a gold and silver medal, maybe even gold and bronze, or gold and no medal at all. For that reason, they encourage their athletes to pay attention to the tiniest details and look for marginal gains wherever possible.

Now, I'm assuming you aren't reading this book in order to scrape five seconds off your parkrun time, but we should all be looking to make improvements in our personal health and well-being wherever possible. The reason that I'm mentioning the aggregation of marginal gains at this point is that in looking at the five aspects of SHEDS, I want you to imagine the overall benefit of making a marginal gain in each of the five areas. Imagine making a quick-win change in each area and then realising you've moved five steps forward.

With that in mind, here is a suggested plan for a quick-win SHEDS strategy.

Sleep – The next time you're awake in the middle of the night and not getting to sleep, get up, go to the toilet, don't look at your phone, go back to bed and try to go (back) to sleep. It may or may not work, but it's more likely to work than just lying there.

Hydration – Keep a one-litre drinks bottle beside you at work and drink at least that amount through the course of the day.

Exercise – Set yourself a target for the next week to do more than you did last week, or more than you would normally do in a week. Even if you just set an initial target of walking one mile more than usual.

Diet – Include some fresh fruit in your breakfast tomorrow and make sure that you achieve your five-a-day, every day for the next week.

Stretching – Stand up straight, stretch your arms above your head, go up onto your tiptoes and see how high you can reach with your fingers.

Those are all very general and may or may not be relevant to you. They are there for indicative purposes only, so adapt them for your own circumstances if necessary. What I'm trying to get across is the idea that you could enjoy significant benefits from making a few small positive changes in the five areas that I've discussed in this chapter.

> However slow you run, you're lapping everyone on the couch.

PART 5

Your Challenge

26

But, what about me? I hear you ask

It's all very well hearing stories of other people's achievements, but where do you begin if you're not into sport? In fact, what do you do if you have never been into sport and positively dislike sport? Or how do you get started if you're overweight, or maybe so rushed off your feet that you just feel unable to find time for exercise?

Well, let's consider a few basic principles. You don't have to take part in sport to benefit from a bit more exercise, physical activity or movement. Walking to work or the shops isn't a sport, but it is exercise, it is physical activity, and a bit more exercise and activity in your life can make a huge difference to your health and well-being. Likewise, cycling to work or cycling with your family isn't a sport either, but it too is a great way of exercising. Walking and cycling as a family activity is also a great way to convey the message to the younger generation that outdoor exercise and physical activity is the basis of a healthy lifestyle and it places parents in the positive light as being good role models.

Most people have to commute to and from work and most of us spend time with family and partners, so with a bit of thought and forward planning it should be possible to build some exercise into our lives by looking for ways to introduce more walking and/or cycling into our work journeys, or evenings and weekends with our loved ones.

Alternatively, you might want to get involved in some kind of challenge to walk so many steps or kilometres in the week or month, or perhaps contribute towards your office target for steps taken or distance walked.

Remember, the recommended level of activity is at least 150 minutes per week, and I would certainly agree that everyone should aim for that, but for someone currently taking fewer than 30 minutes per week, an increase to 60 would be a big improvement.

In the majority of cases where someone has increased their level of exercise as a way of improving their life, the first step was recognising there was an issue they needed to address.

Do you remember the push and pull factors from Chapter 1? Getting started with your new exercise plan is likely to involve a combination of push and pull. Accepting and acknowledging that there is an issue, and that exercise is at least part of the solution, is the push aspect.

You might acknowledge that you are overweight, or suffering from a physical or mental health condition, or fear that you may be heading towards having some kind of issue in the future. Whatever the individual circumstances, that acknowledgement represents the push factor. What is often described as the kick up the backside, whether it be from you or your partner or anyone else, is the push to take some action and do something about it.

The good news is that there are boatloads of pull factors out there. Loads of books (including this one), websites (including findtimeforexercise.com), healthcare professionals, personal trainers, parkruns, role models, charities, government agencies and so on, all providing support in one form or another.

This section of the book is going to look at some of the support that is available to you. I say *some*, because there are just so many forms of support that it would be impossible to mention everything that exists at the time of writing, let alone what might come along afterwards.

DIY or Off-the-shelf

In terms of looking for an exercise challenge, there are two basic starting points – either a Do-It-Yourself (DIY) or Off-the-shelf.

The DIY option is one where you use your imagination to make up your own rules to invent your own challenge. Alternatively, an Off-the-shelf option is where you get involved in an initiative that is being promoted to the public, such as the Step Count Challenge, Couch to 5K or one of the national projects like Run Together, Jogscotland or Run Wales.

Supervision

A lot of people feel a sense of reassurance if they have some kind of supervision with their exercise. This can range from paying for the services of a personal trainer or seeking assistance from a healthcare professional in order to have someone set their targets, monitor their progress and provide them with ongoing motivation, right through to joining a club or just pairing up with a friend.

Research into the recovery of patients with type 2 diabetes has shown that physical activity consultations, delivered by a skilled health professional, can be a feasible method of supporting people with diabetes to change their physical activity behaviour[54].

Healthcare supervision can include the use of techniques like motivational interviewing for exercise[55], which are often used by trained specialists to provide guidance and support to those in need of supervised physical activity.

Ask your doctor if you are looking for this kind of support or search online for a local personal trainer.

Building exercise into your daily routine

I often hear people say, "It's alright for you" or "It's alright for him or her over there," followed by, "but I just don't have time for exercise".

My response is that it's not about having time, it's about finding time.

Remember, "Those who do not find time for exercise will have to find time for illness". As Chris said in his interview, "It's as simple as that really".

Another piece of advice to ponder on is this: If you're doubtful about being able to find the time, don't let your circumstances control you, control your circumstances.

One of the main aims of this book is to provide you with practical ideas to help you find time for exercise.

This final part of the book, *Your Challenge*, is going to present a wide range of those ideas, which I hope you will be able to learn from and put into practice in your own situation.

Finding time for exercise, in my view, is a three-stage

process. Firstly, to recognise the need to take more exercise, secondly to make a plan as to how you are going to do it, and then thirdly to put that plan into action.

I like the joke that goes, "How many psychiatrists does it take to change a lightbulb? One, but the lightbulb has to want to change." I see myself a bit like the psychiatrist in that joke, in that I can help you to take more exercise and hopefully improve your life if, and only if, you are able to recognise the need for change. Once you have recognised the need for change, the need to build more exercise into your life, then stage one is complete.

You have already read about my plan and those of the people in the in-depth interviews, so that should have given you a few ideas for a plan, but this section of the book is going to provide you with a lot more ideas that you could adopt or adapt for yourself. So, if you recognise the need to take more exercise and want to make a plan, you're in the right place.

Then, in terms of putting your plan into action, you will need to focus on staying focused. Using exercise as a way of looking after yourself is like anything else in life, you have to work at it, and then keep working at it. You can't do a bit and then say you've done it; you have to keep going, keep working at it, day after day, month after month and year after year. It's hard work, but incredibly rewarding. Just like studying, succeeding in a job, having a rewarding relationship, or anything else in life, you just have to keep on keeping on. As Albert Einstein said, "Life is like riding a bicycle. In order to keep your balance, you must keep moving."

Another beautiful quote that is worth considering came from Martin Luther King Junior. "If you can't fly, then run, if you can't run, then walk, if you can't walk, then crawl, but whatever you do, you have to keep moving forward."

Thinking about keeping moving, you may well choose a challenge that requires you to walk or cycle five, four or perhaps only three days a week, but that doesn't stop you seeking opportunities for a bit of quick exercise on the other days of the week. Let's say your challenge is to walk a mile, four days a week. If that is more than you do right now, and you feel it will challenge you to do it, then that is great, but you could also just look for opportunities to perform a quick two-minute exercise routine once or twice a day on the other days of the week when you don't go for a walk.

Once you start to think more about exercise, just look for those quick opportunities as well as for the longer walks, runs, bike rides or whatever you choose to get into. Basically, do what you can to build exercise into your daily routine.

Setting a target

When it comes to setting your own target, it's far too easy to think you have to be overly ambitious and set a challenge that will really stretch you, and in doing that you might just stretch yourself to the point where you set yourself up to fail within the first couple of weeks. The interviewees in this book made some very good points in this respect. Sam's advice was "Keep it simple" and Jenny said, "It's about making small changes". I would certainly encourage you to use your imagination but give your imagination a reality check, especially in the early days. Don't forget, you can do what I did in terms of changing the rules as you go along if you find you have bitten off more than you can chew or feel that you could chew a bit more.

The next chapter will look at some examples of challenges that could be adopted or adapted, but before going into that detail, all those challenges could be assigned to a category as follows:

- Time   e.g. to run a parkrun in under 30 minutes.
- Distance   e.g. to cycle 2,022 kilometres in 2022.
- Number   e.g. to take the stairs to the 7th floor, at least 200 times in 2022.
- Streak   e.g. to walk at least one mile every day, for as long as possible.
- Mix 'n'   e.g. to run at least one mile every day and run match   at least 20 parkruns in the year.

If you set a target like running a parkrun in under 30 minutes, and you go out one day and achieve that target, then you will hopefully want to set a new target. That may be to run a parkrun in under 29 minutes, but it might be something completely different like running 500 miles in the next year or cycling to work 100 times in the calendar year.

Also, don't be afraid to revise your target if it turns out to be too easy, too difficult, too boring or you just think of something more appropriate for your circumstances. If you set out to cycle 2,022 kilometres in 2022 and find you're on target to complete the distance by the end of July, then you could switch your kilometres to miles and give yourself a harder target to aim for.

When you do find a challenge that is right for you, you are likely to feel a real buzz from that competitive element inside that kicks in and makes you want to achieve a goal. If you do find yourself in that exciting phase of absolutely loving a new challenge and feeling good about it, and good about yourself, then embrace it and do all you can to maintain the enthusiasm, develop a strategy to hold the behaviour and turn your challenge into a long-term habit.

By the time you finish reading this book, I hope you will have seen something that makes you think, "That's the challenge for me" or "That's the basis of my challenge".

You can be an inspiration for other people

We all know what it is like to be inspired by someone in the public spotlight, whether that be a sportsman or woman, a public figure on the television, or someone who has written a book or magazine article. We might also be inspired by someone in our local community, someone who is in no way famous, but someone who has done something that makes us look up to them and provide us with a feeling of wanting to learn from them or copy a bit of what they've done. Whoever it is that gives you that inspiration, you perhaps get a feeling of wanting some kind of version of what they have done.

Now, can you imagine what it might be like if the person providing inspiration to others is you? Even if you do something that appears to be quite simple and not very newsworthy, it might be sufficient to inspire someone else who thinks, "Well done, I think I could do that, or at least a variation of that". Imagine if you started walking a mile every day. After two or three weeks there could be someone in your local community thinking, "Well, if she/he can do that, then I should try to copy her/him – I'm going to start today".

Right now, at this moment in time, you may not realise how you have the potential to not only take on a challenge yourself and become more physically active, but in doing so you might actually become the inspiration for someone else to copy your great example.

A nice phrase that I heard recently was, "The greatest medicine is to teach people how not to need it". If you become more physically active and your actions encourage someone else to increase their activity levels, then you might just have become their teacher that helps them take exercise instead of medicine.

Just as Mark Beaumont cycling round the world might be the inspiration for you to cycle to work more often, your cycling to work more often might be the inspiration for one of your colleagues to go out for a lunchtime walk every day. You might think of your exercise challenge as being fairly low-key and just a personal challenge, but to someone else it might be the spark that ignites their determination to set themselves a challenge and put them on the road to gaining the many benefits of a more active lifestyle.

PRINCIPLE NUMBER 6

However much exercise you currently take, even a small increase in your level of activity could provide you with benefits to your health and happiness.

PRINCIPLE NUMBER 7

Build exercise into your daily routine.

PRINCIPLE NUMBER 8

Set a measurable target, or series of targets, and don't be afraid to revise your target(s) from time-to-time.

PRINCIPLE NUMBER 9

You can be the inspiration for other people.

27

Suggested routines

You've read the Chief Medical Officers' Guidelines and discovered what other people are doing, including the tactics and psychological tricks they employ to keep themselves motivated, so now it is time for you to consider what target you might want to set yourself. Whether you are aiming for an Olympic gold medal (good luck if you are, by the way) or you just plan to stand up and stretch your arms whenever the weather comes on the TV, there is a challenge out there somewhere (probably in-between those two extremes) that you could set for yourself, enjoy working towards and derive real benefits from.

The reason for reminding you about the Chief Medical Officers' Guidelines is to get you to think about the 150 minutes of moderate exercise, 75 minutes of vigorous exercise or a combination of moderate and vigorous activity each week, plus the muscle strengthening exercise at least twice a week that is recommended for people aged 19 to 64. This might be an appropriate time to flick back to Chapter 7 to read through those guidelines again.

Moderate exercise means that you should feel warm and

slightly breathless, but still able to hold a conversation. If you use walking as the basis of your exercise challenge, then try to pick up the speed some of the time. Walking faster gets the heart rate going faster, so don't just saunter along at a slow pace. You don't have to turn into a race walker or power walker, but do try to vary the pace and be aware of your heart rate rising when you do go a bit faster. If you begin to struggle to hold a conversation, then you are likely to be moving from the moderate exercise zone into vigorous exercise. For further information on your heart rate in exercise, there is some helpful information on the British Heart Foundation[56] website.

Remember, it's *my challenge, my rules*, which means it's *your challenge, your rules*. Choose one of these suggestions, or (and this is far more likely) use one of these suggestions to twist, tweak or manipulate into your own personal challenge.

- Don't let the kids have all the fun. Follow their lead and walk the Daily Mile.
- Walk 3 kilometres, 250 days a year.
- Walk 1,000 kilometres in the year.
- Walk 365 miles in the year.
- Cycle 1,000 miles in the year.
- Cycle 2,022 kilometres in 2022 (or equivalent for future years).
- Walk and cycle 1,000 miles in the year.
- Walk the equivalent of a marathon (26.2 miles or 42.2 kilometres) every month.
- Walk for at least 20 minutes every day.
- Take the stairs to the 7th floor, 200 times in the year.
- Get off the bus one stop early, 150 times in the year.

- Go for a 15-minute lunchtime walk, 3 days a week.
- Bike to work 100 times in the year.
- Run 22 parkruns in 2022.
- Run at least one parkrun every month.
- Run at least 10 different parkruns in 2022.
- Run, walk or cycle at least 3 kilometres, 4 times a week.
- Run, walk and cycle a total distance of 20 kilometres a week.
- 20 press-ups every day.
- 1 minute plank every day.
- 5 minutes of stretching every day.
- 3 minutes of step exercises, 3 days a week.
- Sit down and stand up ten times, as fast as possible, 4 times a week.
- Get out of breath every day.
- Get out of breath at least 3 times a week.
- Park, or get off the bus, at least one kilometre away from your work or place of study and walk 15 minutes each way, in other words 30 minutes per day, for five days a week, which equals 150 minutes per week. You might also pay less, or nothing, for parking.
- Stand up every time you watch the weather on TV (you'll pay more attention to the forecast if you do).
- Run, walk or cycle at least 150 minutes every week.
- Spend at least half-an-hour outdoors before midday, at least five times a week.
- Adopt a two-minute stretching routine that you perform while cleaning your teeth.

Please note, these examples are just ideas to get you thinking. Let your imagination run free and come up with your own target; or be really adventurous and set yourself a series of targets. A combination of 22 parkruns in 2022 and run or walk 1,000 kilometres in 2022 would make a great challenge, if that is the level you feel you should be aiming for.

Also, remember to revise your target from time-to-time. If you achieve your target of running 22 parkruns in 2022, you might want to raise the bar slightly and run 23 parkruns in 2023, or you might decide to run 22 parkruns in 2022 of which ten have to be away from your usual parkrun. Or you might want to go for a different kind of challenge and make run or walk 1,000 kilometres your target for the whole of 2022. It really is your challenge, so you make up the rules. I just hope you have fun setting and working towards the target and that you gain real benefits from your efforts.

At all times though, try to bear in mind that the key is to be constantly looking to challenge yourself to take more exercise than you were in the past. As long as your time spent reading this book results in you taking more exercise, then I'll be happy, and you should reap the rewards.

The old adage, "Find what works for you and make sure you enjoy it," is one that I subscribe to and recommend you keep in mind.

You may be the kind of person that prefers a more structured format like the Step Count Challenge, or you might want the camaraderie and social support of a workplace challenge, in which case the links in Appendix 1: *Other popular challenges* should point you towards the relevant websites to get you started.

Then again, you may just want to set your own target and do it yourself. In which case, the list shown above should give you a few ideas.

Whichever approach you prefer, think of those alarming statistics in Chapter 3, remember Zoe's determination to work hard to lose weight, consider how much exercise you have taken over the last year and then make your plan and get started.

Additional exercises

Whether you set yourself a DIY challenge or get involved in some kind of Off-the-shelf programme, you might also want to look for additional ways of fitting a bit more exercise into your daily and weekly schedules. You might be planning to go for a walk or a run after work, but that shouldn't stop you squeezing in a two-minute workout at lunchtime. If you've spent your morning sitting at a desk, then a quick exercise before you eat your lunch will get the blood pumping round your body and raise your heart rate for a few seconds. It's just a matter of looking out for that opportunity and making a habit of fitting in additional snippets of exercise.

There is a form of exercise known as High Intensity Interval Training (HIIT), which is aimed at gaining maximum benefit in minimal time. There is a great deal of debate surrounding HIIT and if you type it into a search engine, you can read the arguments for and against. I don't like the idea of taking all your exercise in the form of HIIT, but I do think there is a lot to be gained from adding a few HIIT exercises on top of a core challenge of making a five kilometres journey every day, or running 1,000 miles in the year, or walking a mile every day, or whatever your challenge is.

As an example, on the day I wrote this chapter I cycled eight kilometres at lunchtime, including two 200-metre sprints and a 400-metre uphill sprint. I then spent most of the afternoon sitting at my desk (not good), so at 4.30 I stood in front of a hard chair and sat down then stood up, as fast as possible, 50 times. That got my heart pumping and moved any fluids that had sunk into my legs. That was a HIIT exercise. Another term for this form of exercise is *exercise snacking*. Despite a good workout at lunchtime, I was in need of an exercise snack at 4.30.

If you look around your home and/or workplace there are lots of opportunities for building the occasional HIIT exercise into your daily routine. Here are just a few ideas to get you thinking:

- Running on the spot.
- Star jumps, burpees and lunges.
- Step-ups using the bottom step, or bottom two steps, on a flight of stairs.

Another form of exercise snacking can be to break your walking or other activity into several short sessions rather than one longer session. The consensus of expert thinking suggests that six walks of five minutes duration in your day can be as beneficial as one 30-minute walk. Taking several short walks throughout your day is therefore regarded as exercise snacking and of worthwhile value. If that is the best way to fit exercise into your day, then go for it. Every minute, every move and every step counts.

Exercise during pregnancy

Go back a few years and there was so much advice about

being overly cautious in terms of exercising at various stages in our lives. Don't overdo it when you're young, take it easy when you're old and definitely don't exercise during pregnancy. Much has changed over the last few years and modern thinking is very much along the line of unless there is an overriding reason not to take exercise, then you should be taking regular exercise throughout your whole life journey.

There is some very good advice on the NHS website about exercising during pregnancy[57] and the best thing I can do is to point you in that direction.

28

Choose your own challenge / Pick a number

I couldn't decide whether to call this chapter, *Choose your own challenge* or *Pick a number*, so I inserted a forward slash and used both titles.

Before we run out of pages and reach the end of the book, it must be time for a concluding *call to action*. It's time for you to *Choose your own challenge*.

Also, you must have noticed that most of the challenges in this book include a goal or a target based around a number, hence the challenge to *Pick a number*.

Here is a quick reminder of some of the challenges that have been mentioned:

- Actively travel at least five kilometres a day for 365 days in the year.
- Walk or cycle 1,000 kilometres or miles in the year.
- Take the stairs 100 times in the year.
- Walk one mile, five days a week.

The main reason for encouraging you to think about and take on a challenge based around a number, or numbers, is that you will be more determined to succeed when you have a target and therefore more likely to stick with it, more likely to focus on the target and more likely to really get your teeth into your challenge.

In developing your own challenge, here are a few points to consider.

Activity

Is your challenge going to be based on walking, running, cycling, gym classes, some kind of combination of activities, or something else? For example, your challenge could be based around a sport such as five-a-side football, walking football, squash or any other sport if that is what suits you best. Play walking football at least forty times in the year would be a great target for some people, especially if that is more than you were doing previously.

For the majority of people, the main activity is going to be walking because it is just so simple to fit into your daily schedule, it doesn't cost any money and you can go out and do it at any time of day for any length of time. It is also incredibly effective in terms of providing you with health benefits. Don't underestimate the value of building more walking into your life.

As you start to exercise more and hopefully set yourself a challenge, try to concentrate on it becoming a habit. The easiest way to walk more is to make walking a habit. Likewise, running, cycling or any other form of physical exercise.

Time

What time can you allocate to exercise and which slots in the day and/or week are you going to find to set that time aside? The morning and afternoon commutes, lunchtimes, or is the best time for you going to be in the evenings?

Solo or with others

Are you going to team up with your partner or a friend to take part in this challenge or maybe share the experience with a bunch of colleagues from work, or is your preference to do your own thing in your own time? Consider your own circumstances, the kind of person you are and how your time commitments are likely to impact on whether you can take exercise with other people or whether it will be easier for you to get out by yourself.

Flexibility

How flexible do you want to be with your exercise plan? Saying you will walk 5 miles per week, means you could go for a 5-mile walk at 10.00 p.m. on the 7th day, whereas saying you will walk one-mile every day of the year means you have to get out there by 11.40 p.m. every day.

Some people like the flexibility of trading activity from one day to another while others prefer the rigid approach that says, "It has to be done on the day, and that's how it will be".

Also, don't forget the phrase, *at least*. You can say, "I will walk *at least* 5 miles per week". If that is your target, then you will usually walk more, but you know that your minimum target is always to walk at least 5 miles.

SMART

A widely accepted method for setting goals is to make them SMART, which stands for Specific, Measurable, Achievable, Relevant and Time Bound.

It is worth thinking about SMART when setting an exercise challenge for yourself.

Specific Your challenge should be clear and easy to understand, and you should be able to focus your efforts on it and generate the motivation to succeed.

Measurable If your challenge is measurable then it will give you a goal to aim for and there should be no doubt as to whether or not you achieved it. That is where the number comes in.

Achievable Don't set out to do the impossible. Be realistic and set an achievable goal, but within that you might want to give some thought to how much you want to challenge yourself. There's a big difference between setting out to run, walk or cycle 1,000 kilometres, compared to 1,000 miles, for example. How far to push yourself, or how high to set the bar, can be the hardest part of setting a challenge, but the point to remember is that you can amend your target, so start small and build up. If you set a challenge then subsequently realise that it's too easy and you're hardly having to stretch yourself, then make it a bit harder; but equally, if you overstretch yourself and realise you've bitten off more than you can chew, then tone it down a bit. It's better to find and set the right goal and stick at it, than admit failure and give up altogether because you overdid it.

Relevant Make sure the challenge you set yourself is relevant to your situation and what you want to achieve from taking more exercise. Also, give some thought to whether you will have the time to take on the challenge. You might want to set a single-activity challenge like walking a certain distance, or you might want to set a multi-activity challenge that encourages you to walk and cycle, and maybe include some running as well. Ask yourself, what is relevant for you?

Time Bound You can set a goal for the next week, then come up with another for the week after that, or you can set a goal for the calendar year, or even just set an ongoing goal to keep going as long as possible.

Putting all that together, you should be able to start thinking of a Specific, Measurable, Achievable, Relevant and Time Bound (SMART) goal for your own personal situation.

Recording

Having set yourself a challenge, the next thing to consider is how you are going to record your progress and know when you've achieved your goal. Options for recording your progress include:

- Diary
- Calendar

- Spreadsheet
- Online (app, group challenge, fitness device, etc.)

You can be as low-tech or sophisticated as you want to be with recording your progress. Some people just tick the box on their calendar when they've done something on that day, whereas others develop elaborate spreadsheets to record every little detail. It's up to you. If you want to keep it simple, then don't feel that you have to do anything fancy. Getting out of the door and actually doing the exercise is far more important than writing about it afterwards, although the ever-expanding spreadsheet can be part of the motivation to keep going.

Motivation

What are you going to do to make sure you stick at it? Here are a few ways to keep your plan on track.

- Start small and build up.
- Challenge yourself, but remember, it's better to be realistic and succeed than aim too high and fail. You can always aim higher if you find your initial challenge too easy.
- Give yourself a reminder of what motivated you in the first place. Re-read this book or watch the Dr Mike Evans video again, or do whatever it was that triggered your original desire to take positive action and enjoy taking more physical exercise.
- Write in your paper or electronic diary or calendar what you need to do.
- Write your exercise goal on your list of things to do in your day.

- Announce the details of your new exercise challenge to your family and/or colleagues.
- Write a blog about your challenge.
- Tell the story to your friends and followers on social media.
- Treat yourself to a series of rewards at various milestones. We're talking about a new running top when you've completed ten weeks of running ten-miles-per-week, not an unhealthy snack after every run.
- Create a series of pop-up reminders on your computer screen to remind you to stand up and go for a walk or take a deskercise break.
- Ask your partner, friend, relative or work colleague to help you with your challenge and let them know when you need help, whether it be to come out running with you or to just be there for a chat when you feel you need some moral support.
- Find a friend to share your challenge with.
- Join a club. This can be great for motivation, tips, support and generally making friends.
- Stick a message on your fridge door.
- Work out when you will reach a significant milestone and focus your efforts on getting to that milestone.
- If you don't like the word *exercise*, use the word *movement* instead, and if you don't like the word *sport*, then use the word *activity*.
- Question whether you need to tweak your challenge to make it more achievable and realistic for you. After all, it is a case of finding what works for you and making sure you enjoy it.
- The element of challenge, and the will to succeed, can be

the motivation to keep going and to make regular exercise part of your routine.

- Your physical exercise challenge needs to become a habit.
- Accept that it is you that has to put in the time and actually do the exercise. As the American entrepreneur Jim Rohn said, "You can't hire someone else to do your push-ups for you".

Also, remember what Sam said in her interview in Chapter 13, "It's about finding something that hooks you, that motivates you".

It is perfectly acceptable, indeed advisable, to revise your target from time-to-time. If you set a target and find it is too easy or too hard, then you can amend it. For example, if you set a walking target, but want to switch it to a multi-activity target, then amend it. The most important points are that you find what works for you, and that you enjoy it and keep doing it.

As Professor Stephen Hawking stated in one of his most famous quotes, "It matters that you don't just give up".

PRINCIPLE NUMBER 10

Find what works for you and make sure you enjoy it.

29

Ten principles

Just before you head out of the door for a brisk walk or pleasant bike ride, here is a quick reminder of the ten principles that have emerged from the preceding chapters.

1. You don't have to copy the person that inspires you. Use your imagination to channel inspiration into your own situation.
2. Sit less – Stand more – Move more.
3. My challenge, my rules – Your challenge, your rules.
4. Get out on the bread-and-butter days, and relish the five-course meal days.
5. Have a winter strategy so that you maintain the motivation through the cold, dark, wet months.
6. However much exercise you currently take, even a small increase in your level of activity could provide you with benefits to your health and happiness.
7. Build exercise into your daily routine.
8. Set a measurable target, or series of targets, and don't be afraid to revise your target(s) from time-to-time.
9. You can be the inspiration for other people.

10. Find what works for you and make sure you enjoy it.

Copy these principles and pin them to your desk at work or stick them to your fridge door with a magnet.

Refer to them often and use them to motivate and remind yourself.

Best of all, read them every single day, put them into practice and reap the rewards.

Epilogue

The COVID-19 pandemic which began in 2020 coincided with the time when I was preparing this book for publication. As I worked my way through the various chapters, making changes and adding new material, the TV and radio news items were constantly referring to people using their one-hour of exercise to run, walk, cycle and connect with nature.

I was extremely heartened by these stories in the sense that there was a common thread running through them, emphasising the importance of regular exercise for our mental well-being as well as our physical health. A phrase that I often noted being used was, "taking our daily exercise," which pleased me greatly, and it didn't escape my notice that many people turned to some amazingly imaginative physical activity challenges to keep fit, protect their mental well-being and even raise money for charity. From Captain Tom walking laps of his garden to record breaking runs around mountain circuits, and from people setting themselves a press-up challenge to others completing a marathon round and round their modest back lawns, the activity challenge was alive and well throughout that otherwise dreadful year.

The exercise challenges and internet fitness classes made the news, but behind the headlines there was actually an increase in inactivity during 2020. Despite so many people getting outdoors for their daily exercise, with the closure of gyms, swimming pools and other recreation facilities, and for some the added difficulty of accessing urban greenspace, there are fears that the pandemic might have fueled an even deeper physical inactivity crisis. There was a sense of fun and camaraderie that flowed from the many challenges, but there was also a more hidden aspect of loneliness and depression on the part of those who simply found it too difficult to get out for any form of exercise.

Whether we, as individuals, took more or less exercise than normal, the pandemic made many of us question what is important in our lives and a common answer centred around our mental and physical health. I believe that many people suddenly had some quiet time to think about what was truly meaningful and of greatest value to them, and in those calm moments recognised the real significance of health and well-being, and perhaps how they had been neglecting those aspects of their lives up to that point.

With so many people saying, "We mustn't go back to life the way we knew it before – things must change for the better," it gave some hope that out of this tragic episode, there should at least be some long-term improvements in the way we prioritise our actions in life. Regular exercise is now higher on the priority list for so many people as a result of COVID-19. It is also higher on the political agenda.

Major moments like this lead to changes at a societal level, and a change that must be grasped is for our civic leaders to develop a much greater focus on physical activity and its links to health. Health and well-being need to be at the heart of our decision making as we move into the post-COVID era, and the ways in which we live our lives and move around must change in ways that remove barriers to physical activity and enable more people to move more often.

As individuals, as well as a society, we need to value our health more than we did previously. A positive outcome will be for the message about finding time for exercise to become more widely recognised than before and for more people to be actively involved in promoting that message.

Finally, the pandemic caused a great deal of pain and suffering, interrupted all of our lives, and is likely to leave each of us with a new set of priorities and revitalised attitude towards our personal health and well-being. I sense a level of cautious optimism that it will lead to opportunities for creating healthier lifestyles. For all of us, especially those that were left behind in 2020 and whose health suffered the most due to the restrictions on our movements, let's not squander those opportunities.

Appendix 1

Other popular challenges

Run Together

Run Together has been created by England Athletics, the membership and development body for grassroots athletics and running in England, to provide friendly, inclusive running opportunities for everyone in England.

Run Together supports people interested in joining a running group or looking to become a run leader. The emphasis is on gentle, non-competitive running and ensuring that everyone is made to feel welcome.

https://runtogether.co.uk/

Jogscotland

Jogscotland is Scotland's recreational running network and part of Scottish Athletics.

It is made up of hundreds of jogging groups located across Scotland, meeting in sports centres, community halls, parks and businesses, and jogging on their local paths, pavements and trails. The emphasis at every Jogscotland group is on enjoying exercise and supporting one another in a friendly atmosphere. Groups are led by qualified Jog Leaders (mostly volunteers), who guide and inspire their members.

Nobody is *too slow* to join Jogscotland. Groups are available for walkers, joggers and runners of all levels, from complete beginners to long-distance runners.

Jogscotland is suitable for healthy adults of all ages – members include joggers in their 80s, a large number who have taken up jogging for the first time later in life, and those who are getting active to help them lose weight. Whatever your age, shape, size or fitness level, you will be made welcome!

Jogscotland has a special partnership with SAMH (Scottish Association for Mental Health) to further the belief in the value of physical activity and sport as a means to achieve both physical and mental well-being.

Jogscotland also has a *Mums on the Run* programme offering guidance, advice and solutions to help mums enjoy the physiological, social and psychological benefits of getting out and being active. You can even take your wee one to class with you in the buggy, so there's no need to worry about arranging childcare while you exercise.

https://jogscotland.org.uk/

Run Wales / Rhedeg Cymru

Run Wales / Rhedeg Cymru is the Welsh organisation that promotes informal, recreational jogging and running. A nationwide network of running groups provides everyone in Wales with the opportunity to become involved in a local running group.

https://irun.wales/

Get Active

Sport Northern Ireland runs a Get Active initiative that is the equivalent resource for those looking to become more active and increase their levels of walking, jogging or running.

http://www.sportni.net/get-active/

Couch to 5K

The Couch to 5K running plan aims to get participants running 5K in nine weeks, even if they have never run before. The plan is delivered via the One You app.

https://www.nhs.uk/live-well/exercise/couch-to-5k-week-by-week/

The Step Count Challenge

The Step Count Challenge is a walking challenge for Scottish workplaces. The aim is simple: walk more and feel the difference. Here's how it works:

- Paths for All run two challenges a year – an 8-week spring challenge and 4-week autumn challenge.
- Enter the challenge in a team of five people.
- The challenge costs £25 per team and you can register one or more teams.
- You get a user account where you record your steps, message your team and track progress on the leaderboards.
- Paths for All set goals and provide regular updates and motivation to keep the registered teams walking.
- They also have lots of competitions and prizes throughout the challenge.

Counting steps is easy. You can use a pedometer, activity tracker or pedometer app on your smartphone.

http://stepcount.org.uk/

Walking for Health

Walking for Health is England's national network of health walk schemes, offering free short walks over easy terrain led by trained walk leaders. The brainchild of GP Dr William Bird MBE, who started leading health walks from his surgery in 1996, Walking for Health is now a national programme. It supports around 600 local schemes across England that deliver a range of group walks for over 75,000 regular walkers.

Since April 2012, the Walking for Health national centre has been run by the Ramblers and Macmillan Cancer Support. The local schemes are run by a variety of organisations including councils, NHS, charities and voluntary groups.

https://www.walkingforhealth.org.uk/
http://www.ramblers.org.uk/go-walking/get-healthy/
walking-for-health.aspx

Health Walks

Health Walks is a network of community-based walks across Scotland aimed at providing free, accessible, low-level exercise for those seeking the benefits of being physically active. Developed and operated by Paths for All, the Health Walks scheme has trained and supported over 10,000 volunteer Walk Leaders who lead over 500 Health Walks every week.

https://www.pathsforall.org.uk/pfa/health-walks/health-walks.html

One Running Movement
One Running Movement is a series of Half Marathon and Marathon distance runs, open to school age children from 4 to 12 years old through Schools Running Movement and all ages from 13+ with One Running Movement.

Each of the distances is cumulative, meaning that the miles are completed one-by-one over a half term if done via a school entry, or in your own time with family or friends if done via a direct entry. Miles or kilometres run as part of the Daily Mile or junior parkrun, or in school PE lessons can be counted towards the cumulative totals.

The final 1.1 mile for cumulative Half Marathon or final 1.2 miles for cumulative Marathon, can be run at one of a series of nationwide live events in front of teachers, family and friends, and where One Running Movement offer a full race experience including race bibs, a marshalled route, music, commentary, a finish line gantry and a medal. There is also the option to complete the events fully virtually.

All participants receive rewards along the way to keep them motivated, such as a tracker chart, achievement chart, wristband and technical T-shirt.

A 10-kilometre option is also being developed.

https://www.onerunningmovement.com/

Scottish Workplace Journey Challenge
This initiative, organised by Sustrans and Transport Scotland, takes place through the month of March each

year, with the aim being to encourage people to travel to work by walking, cycling, public transport and lift-sharing. Anyone who works in an organisation in Scotland can take part and compete for prizes. This fun challenge appeals to a wide range of participants and gets people thinking about their journeys to work as well as journeys within work, for example to meetings. Some people have started walking a one-mile journey to work, while others have cycled to and from meetings 100 miles from their usual office base.

Walking Football

Walking football is different to regular Association Football in many ways and is aimed at the over 50s age group, and many tournaments are now catering exclusively for the over 60s age group.

It has very specific rules that outlaw all running and allows no contact between players. Over-head height restrictions and indirect free kicks ensure that the sport is played safely with full consideration to the participants' age.

Teams are either 5- or 6-a-side. As a result of these rules, games are played at a slower pace, often on state-of-the-art artificial pitches, thus reducing the threat of pain, discomfort and injury, with players briskly walking through matches. This allows people who have loved the sport all their lives to once again get back to playing safely and introduces the sport to people who perhaps never considered playing before.

https://thewfa.co.uk/
https://www.pathsforall.org.uk/pfa/projects/walking-football.html

The Diabetes UK 1 Million Step Challenge

This charity-led scheme encourages participants to push themselves out of their comfort zone and take one million steps over three months and get sponsored for every stride.

Walk it. Jog It. Dance it. The choice is yours. You will need to take at least 10,000 steps a day to reach your million, so do it your way.

You can take on the challenge alone, or better still, get your family, friends and colleagues involved. You can even split the million steps between a team to make it easier.

https://www.diabetes.org.uk/Get_involved/Fundraising-events/million-step/

The Marcothon

The Marcothon is quite a challenge to undertake. Do not underestimate it and don't get talked into this one if your running experience amounts to a few short jogs over the last three or four weeks and someone on Facebook claims you'll be able to take on the Marcothon.

The Marcothon, for anyone who hasn't heard of it before, is the challenge to run at least three miles (or 25 minutes if that comes first) every day throughout the month of December.

The Marcothon started in 2009, when Marco Consani challenged himself to run every day in November. His wife Debbie decided to follow suit and run every day in December. She then posted the challenge – dubbing it the Marcothon – and before long there was a group of runners equally eager to embrace the winter conditions of December 2009. In 2010, the group was added to Facebook and attracted over 500 runners from across the globe. In 2015, there were nearly

6,000 and the popularity of this challenge is increasing with every passing year.

If you were to challenge yourself to run every day in a calendar month, you probably wouldn't choose December. After all, it's the darkest month (in the northern hemisphere), the longest month (equal with six others), one of the wettest, coldest and stormiest months of the year, and it is the month when the typical person consumes the most alcohol and rich food.

Given that all those who accept the Marcothon challenge have to contend with the wet, the cold, the darkness, the parties, the food, the drink and their family, and still keep stepping into their running shoes each day actually makes December the perfect month for such a challenge. It is all about being tactical in terms of finding somewhere to run when it is icy, getting out before the relatives come round to visit and getting out in daylight whenever you can manage to fit in your run before 4.00 p.m.

Ok, I've thrown a few negatives in there for comedic effect, but the positive, the factor that pulls a lot of runners through the challenge, is the supportive Marcothon community. The camaraderie within clubs and on social media and online forums is such that those taking on the challenge often say that their friends got them through it.

Having set out to run the Marcothon myself in 2016, only to slow to a walk on day seven due to a stiff back, I was more determined than ever to succeed in 2017. On my second attempt I managed to get through it, and can confirm that it was tough, but rewarding and worth the effort.

Due to its popularity on social media, the Marcothon has developed a special lexicon. Here are a few terms and phrases that refer to certain Marcothon tactics, but which could also be used in pursuing other physical challenges.

A *Double Dunt* is where someone goes out for a run at about 11.30 p.m., runs at least 3 miles or 25 minutes, then resets their watch at midnight and runs for another 3 miles or 25 minutes, thereby ticking off two days in one run.

A *Jungle Book* is where you just do the *bare necessity* (3 miles or 25 minutes) and no more.

Twitter: @themarcothon
Facebook: There is a public group under the name of Marcothon followed by the year, e.g. Marcothon 2021.

On the basis of not having to copy the person that inspires you and using your imagination to set your own exercise challenge, you could create a new challenge of your own based on doing something every day in December. If your name is Samantha and you decide to challenge yourself to walk a mile every day in December, then why not call it the Samanthathon, or if your name is Ron and think you could spend 10-minutes on a rowing machine every day in December, then call it the Ronathon and get rowing. It's a case of your challenge – your rules, so why not use the Marcothon idea to come up with your own festive challenge?

RED January

RED January stands for Run Every Day in January. The emphasis with this challenge is on the mental health benefits of just being active every day throughout the month of January whether you run, walk, cycle, swim, play football or take part in whatever physical activity you prefer. The challenge is to be physically active on all 31 days of January.

RED January aims to provide participants with a goal and focus to help people through a characteristically tough month. Furthermore, RED January can empower, educate and support you to start the year as you mean to go on, forming healthy habits to continue throughout January and beyond.

https://redtogether.co.uk/
Twitter: @REDJanuaryUK

Fizz Free February

Following on from challenges in December and January, Southwark Council in London has come up with a novel challenge for the month of February.

Could you and your family give up fizzy drinks for February?

Taking part in Fizz Free February is a great way to reduce your sugar intake by cutting out fizzy drinks. It can also help you on your way to drinking less sugary drinks for the rest of the year.

Hashtag: #FizzFreeFebruary

So, as we've just seen, there are ready-made challenges for December, January and February. How long will it be before we have nine more and there's one for every month of the year? Does anyone fancy inventing the Marchathon?

Runstreak

A runstreak is when a person runs at least a mile, every calendar day without fail. Ron Hill set the current record for runstreaking at 52 years and 39 days, and many others are now busy following his lead and setting their own runstreak records. There are international and UK lists of runstreaker achievements, so you can monitor how you are comparing to your fellow streakers.

https://www.runeveryday.com/int-active-streaks.php

Exercise Streak

Ok, I'll admit to inventing this one myself, but let's see if it catches on. An exercise streak is the challenge of making an active journey of at least five kilometres every calendar day without fail. An exercise streak can use as many forms of active travel as your imagination can come up with. Running, walking and cycling are likely to form the basis of an exercise streak, but I also include canoeing, kayaking and skiing in mine. Others might choose to add swimming and/or rollerblading to their list and those with a disability might include wheelchairs, handcycling and/or tricycling.

I would love to hear from any other exercise streakers. Who knows, sometime in the future we could maybe have a list along the lines of the runstreakers' league table.

Everesting and other cumulative height gain challenges

The Everesting challenge is a simple concept that is incredibly difficult to complete. It is mainly for cyclists, but can be undertaken on foot. The challenge is to climb the equivalent height of Mount Everest (8,848 metres or 29,029 feet) in the shortest possible time by repeatedly riding (or running or walking) up and down the same hill.

https://everesting.cc/

Similar challenges are common and tend to be the result of someone's active imagination. You can challenge yourself to climb the height of Everest over the course of a month or over the length of a year's hill racing, for example.

Of course, the climbing challenge doesn't have to use Mount Everest as its benchmark. Some people set out to climb the height of Mont Blanc, Ben Nevis or Snowdon over the course of a year by taking the stairs instead of the lift at their workplace.

In the summer of 2020, a 90-year-old lady in a Scottish care home succeeded in climbing the height of the shapely mountain, Suilven (731 metres or 2,399 feet), by climbing the care home stairs 282 times, and raising £350,000 for charity.

Like with many other physical challenge categories, there is within the cumulative height gain challenges a wide spectrum from the apparently easy (but perhaps not for the person taking on the challenge) right through to the fiendishly hard.

496 Challenge

This is a seriously difficult challenge that some extremely fit people might like to attempt in a month with 31 days. The challenge is to run the number of kilometres in the date, or if you want to make it really difficult – miles, on each day of the month. So, on the first day of the month you run one kilometre/mile, two on the second, three on the third, all the way up to 31 on the 31st. The total distance you need to run in the month adds up to a massive 496 kilometres or miles. The challenge begins with an easy first week, but the severity ramps up through the middle of the month and ends with a series of very long runs in the last week.

This is an adaptable challenge in that an individual might like to add their own twist to it. One option could be to place the numbers 1 to 31 in a hat, and on each morning of the month pick a number out of the hat and run that number of kilometres or miles. That *tombola* way of mixing up the distances would add an element of surprise, avoid the frantic final week but still add up to that daunting total of 496.

This Girl Can

Funded by The National Lottery and developed by Sport England, This Girl Can is an initiative aimed at helping women overcome the fear of judgement that is stopping too many women and girls from joining in with sport and other physical activities.

http://www.thisgirlcan.co.uk/

Newcastle Can

Newcastle Can is a city-wide campaign to encourage residents of Newcastle-upon-Tyne to adopt a healthier and fitter lifestyle. The original aim was for the city to collectively lose 100,000 pounds in one year.

The campaign is a partnership between Newcastle City Council and celebrity chef, food writer and environmental campaigner Hugh Fearnley-Whittingstall.

https://www.newcastle.gov.uk/services/public-health/healthier-city/newcastle-can

Healthier Fleetwood

The seaside town of Fleetwood on the Lancashire coast has

alarmingly high rates of a series of illnesses and one of the lowest life expectancy rates in the country. It doesn't take a great deal of imagination to suspect a causal link between the two outcomes. Healthier Fleetwood is a community-led initiative aimed at tackling the underlying physical and mental health problems.

What began in spring 2016 is now an active project working in partnership with agencies, connecting residents and organising a wide range of activities. The community approach to addressing health issues has triggered media attention and this has led to the progress of Healthier Fleetwood being tracked by the BBC News programme.

As with Newcastle Can, the city- or town-scale initiative is an interesting model that looks set to be copied, adapted and developed in all kinds of directions over the coming years. I can't wait to see where this type of initiative will go in the future, which places will come on board and who the individuals will be that get the projects off the ground. Perhaps you're the person to start something in your community.

https://www.healthierfleetwood.co.uk/

Beat the Street

Beat the Street is an imaginative programme that has been developed by Intelligent Health, the innovative health technology company founded by Dr William Bird MBE. Intelligent Health aims to change the behaviour of the most inactive people in society and build active communities through campaigns, social prescribing and supplying personal activity trackers.

The highest profile programme that Intelligent Health has

run is Beat the Street, a point-scoring game that encourages residents in a particular area to tap a series of electronic pads known as Beat Box sensors with their card or fob. The game requires people to walk, run or cycle between Beat Box sensors and accumulate points for each sensor they visit. The game triggers a competitive spirit in people, resulting in them moving more and sitting less. As well as being a fun activity for families, it is also popular with workplaces and competitions are held between different organisations.

http://www.intelligenthealth.co.uk/

National Fitness Day

National Fitness Day, held in September each year, is an initiative run by ukactive. The aim is to encourage the nation to celebrate the fun of fitness and highlight the benefits of being physically active. Check out the website, make a note of the date and consider getting involved. Then, act on the fun you have that day and make an effort to become more active afterwards.

https://www.nationalfitnessday.com/

Recovery Ramblers

Recovery Ramblers is an initiative in the Forth Valley region of Scotland aimed at helping people with obsessive behaviours such as alcohol, drug and gambling addictions. Started in April 2016 by the Forth Valley Recovery Community and funded by the charitable company Addiction Support and Counselling, the Recovery Ramblers project aims to address physical and mental health issues by promoting improved diets and physical activity.

In its first two and a half years the initiative has helped over 500 individuals and there have been around 12,000 separate visits made to their recovery cafés in Stirling, Falkirk and Alloa. These cafés are staffed by 6 professionals and a team of 25 volunteers. Their programme of health walks are attended by an average of about 7 people for each walk, plus there are other activity sessions including climbing, curling, yoga and soft archery.

The Forth Valley Recovery Community is active on social media and can be found at: Facebook.com/forthvalleyrecoverycommunity and on Instagram at: Instagram.com/forthvalleyrecoverycommunity. A common theme amongst the messages posted on these sites is, "I wish there was something like this in our area".

https://www.sfad.org.uk/service/forth-valley-recovery-community-falkirk-recovery-ramblers

National Walking Month

Living Streets is the national charity that aims to promote walking and improve the walking environment. One of the Living Streets campaigns is to promote May as National Walking Month. They also promote Walk to School Week towards the end of May.

https://www.livingstreets.org.uk/

Play on Pedals

Play on Pedals began in 2004, with the aim of giving every pre-school child in Glasgow the opportunity to learn to ride a bike before starting school. The project is a partnership between Cycling UK, Cycling Scotland, The Glasgow Bike Station and

Play Scotland. It was the first of its kind in the UK, offering city-wide provision to pre-school children and their families.

http://playonpedals.scot/

British Heart Foundation Challenges

My Step Challenge is run by the British Heart Foundation and is similar to the Step Count Challenge.

https://www.bhf.org.uk/how-you-can-help/fundraise/my-step-challenge

The British Heart Foundation has another initiative in the form of the Stair Climb Challenge. As the name suggests, this challenge encourages staff members to increase their use of the stairs and the target is often to climb the equivalent of a well-known mountain or building.

https://www.bhf.org.uk/publications/health-at-work/health-at-work-stair-climb-challenge

The British Heart Foundation website contains a long list of other physical challenges and the following page contains links to some great events that are well worth reading about.

https://www.bhf.org.uk/how-you-can-help/events

Workplace Challenge

Workplace Challenge is an initiative aimed at encouraging more workplace sport and activity.

http://www.workplacechallenge.org.uk/

Walking Home for Christmas

This walking challenge, held in December each year, is organised by the Walking With The Wounded charity and raises funds for ex-servicemen and women in urgent need of mental health care.

https://www.walkinghomeforchristmas.com/

Love to Ride

This is a great initiative aimed at getting more people cycling, more often. Their website has useful information for workplaces looking to sign up for their various challenges, including their flagship challenge, Cycle September.

www.lovetoride.net/uk

The Virtual Journey Challenge

Another great workplace challenge is the virtual journey. Your team of workers can create a virtual journey challenge by setting out to walk the equivalent distance of a long-distance route such as the Pennine Way or West Highland Way, or the distance between two cities, such as Edinburgh to London or London to Paris, or to use the stairs to climb the equivalent height of a high mountain such as Ben Nevis or Mount Everest. Teams of a given number of staff can compete to see which team completes the distance or height gain first.

Yorkshire Bike Library

The Yorkshire Bike Library scheme is a legacy of the annual Tour de Yorkshire cycle race, and thousands of people across the county are now benefiting from the project. Old bikes are donated to the scheme, then refurbished by prisoners as part of their training and rehabilitation, before the bikes are lent out to school children via a bike library. At the time of writing there were 49 bike libraries, supported by 63 donation stations. As children grow, they simply return their bike to the library and take out a bigger bike. The scheme also organises events and activities such as cycling lessons, family activities, guided rides and bike maintenance lessons. Larger bikes are also made available for adults to purchase.

http://bikelibraries.yorkshire.com/

Cycle 4 Health

Cycle 4 Health is designed to aid recovery from long- or short-term physical or mental health conditions. It also offers people who haven't had the chance to cycle the opportunity to give it a try. Over 12 weeks, participants receive expert cycle tuition, develop their cycling skills and go on led bike rides within a small and inclusive group. The project is currently run from a variety of sites in West Yorkshire including community centres, leisure centres and social enterprise hubs where all equipment is provided. Many people attending don't have access to a bike, so this helps to clear this initial barrier. The weekly structure is flexible and is driven entirely by the abilities of those attending.

The main route onto the programme is via referral from a professional within a health setting. This may be a local GP, health worker, case worker, an exercise team (usually within a local authority) or a healthy-eating adviser who considers that 12 weeks of cycling and activity will have a positive effect on a person's mental or physical well-being.

Cycle 4 Health is currently being delivered by Cycling UK on behalf of the West Yorkshire Combined Authority City Connect project. It has three targets:

- To increase participant activity levels thereby improving their health and well-being.
- To change participant travel behaviour by offering cycling as a mode of transport.
- To offer opportunities to cycle where it otherwise would not be possible.

https://www.cyclinguk.org/community-outreach/health

The Conqueror Event Series

This is a virtual fitness challenge that originated in the USA and is now operating in the UK. It is aimed at both individuals and teams. The idea is to cover the distance of a journey of your choosing. So, you can run, walk, cycle, row and/or swim the length of Route 66 (2,200 miles), or the length of Britain (1,083 miles), over 3, 6, 9 or 12 months. Distances are logged manually via the web or smartphone app, or direct from a range of fitness devices.

https://www.theconqueror.events/

Get Britain Standing

The Get Britain Standing website (and equivalent websites in other nations) is a fantastic resource for information relating to the benefits of standing and moving, plus a range of ideas for taking practical action to get out of sedentary habits.

http://www.getbritainstanding.org/

One You Active 10 Walking Tracker

This downloadable free smartphone app from Public Health England encourages you to take a brisk 10-minute walk each day.

https://www.nhs.uk/oneyou/active10/
https://www.nhs.uk/better-health/get-active/

Massive Open Online Courses (MOOC)

The Sit Less, Get Active MOOC is run by Edinburgh University. This free online course helps you learn how to monitor your own activity and set physical activity goals.

https://www.coursera.org/learn/get-active

The Canada 150 Exercise Challenge

This challenge from Canada is organised by the Healing and Cancer Foundation. The aim is for those signing up to the scheme to take 150 minutes of fun physical activity every week for the ten weeks of summer.

https://healingandcancer.org/canada150/

Fitness Devices

Fitness tracking devices made by Fitbit, Garmin and Apple have become the technological response to people's need and desire to take more exercise. As well as tracking your progress towards your exercise goals, these devices are able to monitor aspects of your life such as sleep, heart rate and activity levels.

Some people prefer not to use this kind of technology, whereas others find that it motivates them to try harder to reach a goal, whether that be to walk 10,000 steps in a day, go above a certain heart rate each day or cover a target distance in a month. Many people use such devices to record a wide range of data and gain all kinds of motivation from them, so there is no doubt in my mind that such devices must be seen as a valuable contribution towards creating a more active and healthy population.

Appendix 2

An open letter to the four UK transport ministers

The following is an open letter addressed to four transport ministers in the UK: Humza Yousaf, Minister for Transport and the Islands, Scotland; Karen Bradley, MP, Secretary of State for Northern Ireland; Ken Skates, MP, Cabinet Secretary for Economy and Transport, Wales; Chris Grayling, MP, Secretary of State for Transport, England.

The letter was published in the *British Journal of Sports Medicine* on 9 April 2018.

A call to action for safe routes for children

We, as physical activity researchers, clinicians, transport specialists and advocates, call on you to use your powers as a transport minister to drastically step up your programme of infrastructure and behaviour change. This is to help children travel safely and actively for local journeys within their communities by addressing parental/carer fears for their safety.

Such a change requires dedicated funding of at least 10% of the national transport budgets to pay for infrastructure interventions supported by a behaviour change programme. This was first proposed and justified in a report by the Association of Directors of Public Health as long ago as 2008, endorsed by over 100 concerned academic, health, transport and other organisations. Scotland has made a very welcome start with the doubling of funding for active travel from the Scottish Government, announced in 2017. This gives momentum to the local authorities keen to see a step change in active travel, but it is just that, a start. More is needed to raise the UK nations to active travel levels comparable with many mainland European countries. Moreover, public polling suggests that the majority would support such a step change to favour active travel.

We need to take action because children's independent mobility has declined sharply across the UK since the 1970s, when it was first measured. We see this not least in terms of increasing car use for the school journey. This reflects the fact that across these four decades politicians and highway engineers have planned for increased car use. So that is what has resulted. Yet, across the same period we have accumulated much greater scientific evidence for the health impacts of this decline in physical activity. The importance of routine physical activity, such as active travel, for heart health, weight management, and mental well-being are just three of the myriad aspects of health gain which are now routinely denied to children. In the process, we have also exposed them to higher levels of pollution inside vehicles, something largely unknown among parents/carers. Children are then habitualised into car use as the social norm which is likely to influence their adult travel behaviours (and how they raise the next generation).

We are not starting from scratch. There are locations across the UK where infrastructure provision is making it possible for more children to travel actively, although these remain exceptions. Successful UK programmes have occurred recently, not least the Cycle Demonstration Towns and Sustainable Travel Towns programmes in England, the London Cycle Superhighways, and the Smarter Choices, Smarter Places programme in Scotland. These were shown to be highly effective and had excellent benefit to cost ratios, unlike many schemes devoted to expanding the road network capacity for the short-term benefit of car users. In Wales, the Active Travel Act 2013 has concentrated minds on what must follow if the Act is to be shown to have led to a shift in travel behaviour.

If we achieve significant increases in activity among children, then we will have enabled increased travel choices for many adults too. Moreover, the health benefits follow the behaviour so that we know that safer environments for children to travel actively, such as to school, will lead to significant cost savings in the future to the National Health Service, contribute too to carbon reduction targets, and ingrain sustainable travel behaviours among tomorrow's generation of adults. And it will have contributed to a broader set of solutions needed to resolve associated issues, not least urban congestion, poor air quality and public transport reliability.

The rhetoric of improving the environment in favour of children's active travel has been visible for at least two decades but tangible changes have largely been absent from transport planning. We suggest that the time is right to redress the imbalance and give back to today's children many of the freedoms that older adults recall and benefited from in terms of the levels of independent mobility.

Signed

Christopher W Oliver (1), Paul Kelly (1), Dave du Feu (2), Graham Baker (1) and Adrian Davis (3,4).

Author affiliations

1. Physical Activity for Health Research Centre, University of Edinburgh, Edinburgh, UK
2. The Lothian Cycle Campaign, Edinburgh, UK
3. Transport Research Unit, Edinburgh Napier University, Edinburgh, UK
4. Faculty of Business and Law, University of the West of England, Bristol, UK

Appendix 3

National Health Service
5 A Day Guidelines

One adult portion of fruit or vegetables is 80g.

The guide below will give you an indication of typical portion sizes for adults.

Children should also eat at least five portions of a variety of fruit and vegetables a day. The amount of food a child needs varies with age, body size and levels of physical activity. As a rough guide, one portion is the amount they can fit in the palm of their hand.

5 A Day fruit portions
Small-sized fresh fruit
One portion is two or more small fruit, for example two plums, two satsumas, two kiwi fruit, three apricots, six lychees, seven strawberries or 14 cherries.

Medium-sized fresh fruit
One portion is one piece of fruit, such as one apple, banana, pear, orange or nectarine.

Large fresh fruit
One portion is half a grapefruit, one slice of papaya, one slice of melon (5cm slice), one large slice of pineapple or two slices of mango (5cm slices).

Dried fruit
A portion of dried fruit is around 30g. This is about one heaped tablespoon of raisins, currants or sultanas, one tablespoon of mixed fruit, two figs, three prunes or one handful of dried banana chips.

However, dried fruit can be high in sugar and can be bad for your teeth. Try to swap dried fruit for fresh fruit, especially between meals. To reduce the risk of tooth decay, dried fruit is best enjoyed as part of a meal, as dessert for example, not as a between meal snack.

Tinned or canned fruit
One portion is roughly the same quantity of fruit that you would eat for a fresh portion, such as two pear or peach halves, six apricot halves or eight segments of tinned grapefruit. Choose fruit canned in natural juice, rather than syrup.

5 A Day vegetable portions
Green vegetables
Two broccoli spears or four heaped tablespoons of cooked kale, spinach, spring greens or green beans count as one portion.

Cooked vegetables

Three heaped tablespoons of cooked vegetables, such as carrots, peas or sweetcorn, or eight cauliflower florets count as one portion.

Salad vegetables

Three sticks of celery, a 5cm piece of cucumber, one medium tomato or seven cherry tomatoes count as one portion.

Tinned and frozen vegetables

Roughly the same quantity as you would eat for a fresh portion. For example, three heaped tablespoons of tinned or frozen carrots, peas or sweetcorn count as one portion each. For tinned, choose those canned in water, with no added salt or sugar.

Pulses and beans

Three heaped tablespoons of baked beans, haricot beans, kidney beans, cannellini beans, butter beans or chickpeas count as one portion each. Remember, however much you eat, beans and pulses count as a maximum of one portion a day.

Potatoes

Potatoes don't count towards your 5 A Day. This is the same for yams, cassava and plantain too. They are classified nutritionally as a starchy food, because when eaten as part of a meal they are usually used in place of other sources of starch, such as bread, rice or pasta. Although they don't count towards your 5 A Day, potatoes do play an important role in your diet as a starchy food.

5 A Day in juices and smoothies

Unsweetened 100% fruit juice, vegetable juice and smoothies can only ever count as a maximum of one portion of your 5 A Day.

For example, if you have two glasses of fruit juice and a smoothie in one day, that still only counts as one portion.

Smoothies include any drink made up of any combination of fruit/vegetable juice, puree or all the edible pulped fruit or vegetable.

Your combined total of drinks from fruit juice, vegetable juice and smoothies should not be more than 150ml a day – which is a small glass.

For example, if you have 150ml of orange juice and 150ml smoothie in one day, you'll have exceeded the recommendation by 150ml.

When fruit is blended or juiced, it releases the sugars which increases the risk of tooth decay so it's best to drink fruit juice or smoothies at mealtimes.

Whole fruits are less likely to cause tooth decay because the sugars are contained within the structure of the fruit.

Watch out for drinks that say, "juice drink" on the pack as they are unlikely to count towards your 5 A Day and can be high in sugar.

5 A Day and ready-made foods

Fruit and vegetables contained in shop-bought ready-made foods can also count toward your 5 A Day.

Always read the label. Some ready-made foods contain high levels of fat, salt and sugar, so only have them occasionally or in small amounts as part of a healthy balanced diet.

Appendix 4

Twitter Directory

Individuals

Mike Dales	@FindTime4Xrcise
Professor Chris Oliver	@CyclingSurgeon
Dr Andrew Murray	@docandrewmurray
Dr Mike Evans	@docmikeevans
Ben Smith	@the401challenge

Organisations and Challenges

Parkrun	@parkrun
Parkrun UK	@parkrunUK
The Daily Mile	@_thedailymile
NHS Choices	@NHSChoices
NHS England	@NHSEngland
NHS Health Scotland	@NHS_HS
NHS Digital	@NHSDigital
Get Britain Standing	@getGBstanding

Get Scotland Walking	@stepchangescot
Paths for All	@PathsforAll
Step Count Challenge	@step_count
UKActive	@_ukactive
Active Working	@ActiveWorking
Moving Medicine	@movingmedicine
The Marcothon	@themarcothon
RED January	@REDJanuaryUK
Active Cairngorms	@CNPactive
Healthier Fleetwood	@HealthierFltwd
World Obesity	@WorldObesity
Scottish Association for Mental Health (SAMH)	@SAMHtweets
Get Canada Standing	@getCDAstanding
Get America Standing	@getUSAstanding
Get Oz Standing	@getOZstanding
Get NZ Standing	@getNZstanding

Some useful hashtags

#ActiveCommute	#ActiveGirls	#ActiveKids
#ActiveTravel	#Adventures4Health	#BeActive
#BigBikeRevival	#BigWiggle	#BikeToSchool
#CouchTo5K	#CycleSeptember	#CycleToWork
#CycleToSchool	#Cycling	#DailyMile
#DontThinkLimits	#EveryMoveCounts	#Exercise
#ExerciseEveryDay	#ExerciseIsMedicine	#ExerciseWorks
#FindTimeForExercise	#FitAt50	#FitforLife
#Fitness	#FitnessDay	#FizzFreeFebruary
#GetInspired	#GetOutside	#GoFizzFree

#HomeCommute	#KeepMoving	#KeepRunning
#LoveParkrun	#LunchtimeWalk	#MakeYourDayHarder
#Move	#MoveForLife	#MoveMore
#Move2School	#NationalWalkingMonth	#NoExcusesDoTheWork
#OutsideEveryDay	#Parkrun	#ParkrunTourism
#ParkrunTourists	#ParkrunUK	#PhysicalActivity
#RunEveryDay	#RunTogether	#SitLess
#SugarSmart	#ThisIsMyAdventure	#Try20
#Walking	#WalkInWinter	#WalkOnceADay
#WalkThisMay	#WalkToSchool	#WalkToSchoolWeek
#WalkToWork	#Walk1000miles	#WeightLoss
#WorkInProgress	#ZeroQuit	#5KEveryDay

There are lots more and, of course, you can have fun making up your own.

References

1 https://www.rospa.com/home-safety/advice/general/facts-and-figures
2 https://www.youtube.com/watch?v=3F5Sly9JQao
3 Covey, S.R., 2004. *The 7 Habits of Highly Effective People.* Simon & Schuster. London.
4 https://www.nhs.uk/conditions/obesity/
5 https://www.nhs.uk/Tools/Pages/Healthyweightcalculator.aspx
6 https://www.gov.uk/government/publications/health-matters-obesity-and-the-food-environment/health-matters-obesity-and-the-food-environment--2
7 https://www.nationalarchives.gov.uk/doc/open-government-licence/version/3/
8 http://www.nuffieldtrust.org.uk/blog/can-nhs-help-tackle-uk%E2%80%99s-obesity-epidemic?gclid=CPym57bRoNA CFdQaGwodGhwA4A
9 https://www.nao.org.uk/wp-content/uploads/2020/09/childhood-obesity.pdf
10 https://www.diabetes.org.uk/about_us/news/new-stats-people-living-with-diabetes
11 https://www.gov.uk/government/uploads/system/uploads/attachment_data/file/287943/07-1469x-tackling-obesities-future-choices-summary.pdf
12 https://khub.net/documents/31798783/32038776/Adult+obesity+international+comparisons+data+factsheet/5 ac29533-d3f0-4805-b78b-58456d062e0d?version=1.1
13 http://www.ssehsactive.org.uk/userfiles/Documents/obes-phys-acti-diet-eng-2013-rep.pdf

References

14 https://governmentbusiness.co.uk/features/obesity-%E2%80%93-what-are-consequences-your-department

15 https://fullfact.org/health/misquoted-and-misunderstood-have-one-four-people-really-had-mental-health-problem/

16 https://www.mentalhealth.org.uk/statistics/mental-health-statistics-most-common-mental-health-problems#:~:text=The%20poorer%20and%20more%20disadvantaged,problems%20and%20their%20adverse%20consequences.&text=Mixed%20anxiety%20and%20depression%20has,lost%20from%20work%20in%20Britain.&text=One%20adult%20in%20six%20had%20a%20common%20mental%20disorder

17 https://www.independent.co.uk/news/uk/home-news/office-workers-screen-headaches-a8459896.html

18 https://www.juststand.org/the-facts/

19 https://www.monbiot.com/2012/11/19/housebroken/

20 https://www.nhs.uk/live-well/healthy-body/how-to-get-vitamin-d-from-sunlight/

21 https://www.mentalhealth.org.uk/publications/how-to-using-exercise

22 http://www.who.int/ncds/prevention/physical-activity/gappa/

23 https://apps.who.int/iris/bitstream/hand le/10665/336656/9789240015128-eng.pdf

24 https://www.gov.uk/government/publications/health-matters-getting-every-adult-active-every-day/health-matters-getting-every-adult-active-every-day

25 https://assets.publishing.service.gov.uk/government/uploads/system/uploads/attachment_data/file/832868/uk-chief-medical-officers-physical-activity-guidelines.pdf

26 https://www.bbc.co.uk/sport/get-inspired/43501261

27 https://www.mentalhealth.org.uk/publications/fundamental-facts-about-mental-health-2016

28 https://www.sustrans.org.uk/our-blog/personal-stories/2019/personal-stories/why-i-still-love-cycling-at-86-sylvias-story

29 https://www.runnersworld.com/runners-stories/a21605113/weight-loss-transformation-bob-page/
30 https://stepcount.org.uk/2017/05/meet-the-walkers-alain/
31 https://www.encephalitis.info/petes-story
32 https://thedailymile.co.uk/
33 https://blog.dundee.ac.uk/one-dundee/daily-mile/
34 https://blog.parkrun.com/uk/2018/04/24/2017-run-report/
35 http://www.bbc.co.uk/news/video_and_audio/headlines/36288384
36 https://blog.parkrun.com/uk/2017/01/13/so-excited-for-my-year-ahead/
37 https://raceforlife.cancerresearchuk.org/
38 https://blog.parkrun.com/uk/2018/01/17/6374/
39 https://thebloodsugardiet.com/
40 https://www.cyclescheme.co.uk/
41 https://publications.parliament.uk/pa/cm201719/cmselect/cmtrans/1487/148705.htm#footnote-153
42 https://www.gov.uk/drivers-hours/eu-rules
43 http://www.healthyworkinglives.com/advice/workplace-health-promotion/physical-activity
44 https://www.thekennelclub.org.uk/getting-a-dog-or-puppy/
45 http://www.canicross.org.uk/Welcome_to_Canicross_Trailrunners.html
46 http://www.bikejor.com/
47 https://www.nhs.uk/live-well/eat-well/water-drinks-nutrition/
48 https://www.healthline.com/nutrition/how-much-water-should-you-drink-per-day
49 http://www.actiononsalt.org.uk/
50 http://www.actiononsugar.org/
51 https://www.theguardian.com/commentisfree/2018/aug/15/age-of-obesity-shaming-overweight-people
52 https://www.youtube.com/watch?v=NWRl2D_vb8g
53 https://www.youtube.com/watch?v=O5YX5xg8Seg
54 https://wileymicrositebuilder.com/practicaldiabetes/wp-

content/uploads/sites/29/2017/01/OA-Kirk-lsw.pdf

55 https://www.acefitness.org/education-and-resources/
professional/expert-articles/6532/ignite-behavior-change-
with-motivational-interviewing

56 https://www.bhf.org.uk/informationsupport/publications/
heart-conditions/medical-information-sheets/your-heart-
rate

57 https://www.nhs.uk/conditions/pregnancy-and-baby/
pregnancy-exercise/

Acknowledgements

It was a genuine pleasure to chat with the interviewees who contributed so much to this book and to hear their inspiring stories. Thank you for your time and for being so open and honest.

Thank you to Graham Innes and Helen Warburton for providing me with the opportunity to give two presentations about my exercise challenge. Those talks were back in 2015 in Perth and 2016 in Stirling, and they undoubtedly triggered the sequence of events that led to this book being written.

Belated thanks should go to Edward Smith-Stanley (1799-1869), Prime Minister of the United Kingdom, for coming up with the title of this book as far back as the mid-nineteenth century. I have absolutely no idea whether or not he was a good politician, but he did come up with one exceptionally good line, and for that I am very grateful.

In December 2019, I went to a Royal Scottish Geographical Society (RSGS) talk in Dundee. The speaker that evening was the endurance adventurer, Sean Conway. We met at the end of the evening to share a few stories, Sean signed my copy of his book *Hell and High Water*, and then agreed to write the Foreword for mine. I am grateful to Sean for his wise words and independent *stamp of approval* at the start of this book.

Acknowledgements

To my good friend Sarah Halliday, of Sarah Halliday Art, you are an amazing artist – many thanks for producing a spectacular cover design for this book.

Special thanks go to another good friend, Stephen Jenkinson of Access and Countryside Management Limited for his assistance in writing Chapter 24: *Or, get a dog.* There was only one person I was going to for advice when I decided to write a chapter about dogs.

To the team at Matador, thank you for working alongside me to publish this book.

Numerous people provided help and encouragement along the journey towards completing this book and I can't possibly remember every individual that contributed an idea or two, but I would like to record specific thanks to Mark Beaumont, Oliver Crane, Pete Crane, Malcolm Currie, Lily Dyu, Christie Glasbergen, John-James Greig, John 'Yogi' Hughes, Scott Leach, Val Lovatt, Andrew Manson, Dr Andrew Murray, Caroline Ness, Dawn Nisbet, Professor Chris Oliver, Dr Mike Rivington, Will Roberts, Becky Wood and Fin Wycherley.

While on the subject of providing help and encouragement, I must say a special thank you to the members of Perth Road Runners for their camaraderie, contagious humour and outright love for running. With your encouragement, I always seem to push myself up to, and sometimes beyond, my limits.

I would like to record my appreciation for all the great work carried out by so many people, all around the world, in communicating the vital message about the benefits of regular exercise. The global scale of the problems associated with physical inactivity and unhealthy diets are truly monumental, so the determination and dedication demonstrated by all those working to tackle these issues is deserving of our utmost support and recognition. I will be delighted if this book can help a few people to become more active and thereby make a contribution towards the national and global targets for reducing physical inactivity.

Going back to my childhood days, I am grateful to all those who opened a young mind and inspired this boy to get outside and active. The list could be endless, but near the top of that list would be Sir Bobby Charlton, Denis Law, George Best, Dave Bedford, Brendan Foster, Franz Klamer, Doug Scott and Sir Chris Bonington. Closer to home, and for people who inspired me more directly, were my teachers, the main ones being Bill Fletcher, Dave Glew, Brian Walker, Alan East, Graham Laws and John Brown from Woldgate School, and Guy Wilson, Nan Preston, Mr Fisher (sorry, can't remember his first name) and Wendy Sabey/Norman from Melbourne Primary School. I can't believe I've just called them by their first names!

Also from my childhood days, my time spent at cubs, scouts and village youth club played their part in introducing me to the great outdoors, so thank yous all-round to Ethel Wilson, Joan Todd, Arthur Rawlings and Bob Turner.

Higher education played a big part in developing my knowledge, skills and passions in many areas, including the benefits of physical activity and encouraging others to share and discover my love of the countryside, so I would like to record my appreciation for the support I received as an undergraduate at I M Marsh College of Physical Education (now part of Liverpool John Moores University) and postgraduate at Northumbria University.

Acknowledgements

It is with great sadness that Graham Innes, Bill Fletcher and Nan Preston will never see this book in print. They all played their parts in creating the author and this book, and I wanted them to see their names being recognised in this acknowledgement, but sadly Graham and Bill both died in 2019 and Nan passed away in 2020. I would like their families and loved ones to know that I really appreciate the parts that Graham, Bill and Nan played in making this book possible.

Last, but certainly not least, a great big thank you to Fiona Manson for endless hours of fruitful discussion on the topic, as well as sharing many five-course meal days, and quite a few bread-and-butter days as well. Thank you for running uphill marathons with me and being my partner on this amazing journey. ☺

A final thought

I mentioned in the *Preface* a spectrum from the totally inactive to the superfit. We're all on that spectrum, somewhere. Now, imagine if everyone was to become slightly more active and move the equivalent of one percentage point along that line; we would all end up in the same position relative to each other, but we would all gain some benefit from being that little bit more active. The financial savings for the NHS would be enormous and the total number of extra years lived could be phenomenal, but the years lived on medication and under treatment would be vastly reduced and the resultant improvement in quality of lives would be fantastic. If a one percentage increase in everyone's exercise levels could lead to results like that, and I believe it could, then imagine if we could all make a five, or even ten percent improvement. Let's all do our bit.

On that note, writing this book has involved far too much sitting down in front of a computer screen, so I'm going outdoors now to enjoy some serious exercise. Care to join me?

You have reached the very last page of the book.

I hope you enjoyed reading it.

Now go outside and play.